CW00767115

THE MAZE

'THE DETECTIVE STORY CLUB is a clearing house for the best detective and mystery stories chosen for you by a select committee of experts. Only the most ingenious crime stories will be published under the THE DETECTIVE STORY CLUB imprint. A special distinguishing stamp appears on the wrapper and title page of every THE DETECTIVE STORY CLUB book—the Man with the Gun. Always look for the Man with the Gun when buying a Crime book.'

Wm. Collins Sons & Co. Ltd., 1929

Now the Man with the Gun is back in this series of COLLINS CRIME CLUB reprints, and with him the chance to experience the classic books that influenced the Golden Age of crime fiction.

THE DETECTIVE STORY CLUB

FURTHER TITLES IN PREPARATION

THE MAZE

AN EXERCISE IN DETECTION

BY

PHILIP MACDONALD

WITH AN INTRODUCTION BY
JULIAN SYMONS

COLLINS
CRIME
CLUB

COLLINS CRIME CLUB
An imprint of HarperCollins*Publishers*
1 London Bridge Street
London SE1 9GF
www.harpercollins.co.uk

This Detective Story Club edition 2017

First published for The Crime Club
by W. Collins Sons & Co. Ltd 1932

A catalogue record for this book is available from the British Library

ISBN 978-0-00-821637-5

Typeset in Bulmer MT Std by
Palimpsest Book Production Ltd, Falkirk, Stirlingshire
Printed and bound in Great Britain by
Clays Ltd, St Ives plc

MIX
Paper from
responsible sources
FSC™ C007454

INTRODUCTION

THE idea of the crime story in which the solution should be the result of perfectly rational deductions from given facts—an exercise in ratiocination, as Poe called it—was one that preoccupied writers in the 'twenties and early 'thirties, when the crime story was coming of age. It was this dream that the early Ellery Queen books tried to fulfil with their 'Challenge to the Reader' three-quarters of the way through; that was at the heart of John Dickson Carr's locked room mysteries; that was approached at times by writers as various as Anthony Berkeley, Agatha Christie and C. Daly King.

The Maze, which was published in 1932, is Philip MacDonald's contribution to this conception of the totally logical puzzle. It is, he says, 'An Exercise in Detection', and he claims that you are provided with all the evidence on which his detective, Anthony Gethryn, works, and from which he deduces the truth. He says more than this:

> In this book I have striven to be absolutely fair to the reader. There is *nothing*—nothing at all—for the detective that the reader has not had. More, the reader has had his information in exactly the same form as the detective—that is, the verbatim report of evidence and question.
>
> This is a *fair* story.

Does Philip MacDonald claim too much? I don't think so. The facts are clearly laid out, and Gethryn's deductions are admirably logical, beginning with what he calls oddities, and moving from one of these to another to build a case which—if we had spotted the oddities—we could have formulated ourselves. Upon the basis of logic, Gethryn's case is not to be denied, although, as he acknowledges, it is a structure that can be demonstrated but not proved. A perfect crime story, then? Why no, for *The Maze* has the weakness inherent in that desire for a wholly logical crime story, the weakness that we take an interest in the solution to the crime but not in the people who may have committed it. Yet in its time *The Maze* was a notable and underrated crime story, and it remains one of the truly original experiments of the period.

Today Philip MacDonald is almost forgotten, but he and his detective Anthony Gethryn were celebrated figures in the years between the Wars. *The Rasp*, the first crime story he published under his own name, was an immediate success, and *The Noose* (he had a taste for single word titles) was the first Crime Club choice in 1930. The *Evening Standard* bought the serial rights, MacDonald's sales quadrupled, and within a year the Crime Club had 200,000 members. MacDonald continued to produce successful books under several pseudonyms and a number of them were experimental in one way or another. Three of the best were *Rynox, Murder Gone Mad*, and *X v Rex*, the last of which was written under the pseudonym of Martin Porlock. The construction of these books is sometimes careless, but they all contain extremely ingenious ideas, and the desire to do something new is always apparent. Then, in the early 'thirties, MacDonald was invited to Hollywood by RKO Pictures, became a scriptwriter, and wrote little more except for the screen, although he produced in 1952 a collection of short stories called *Fingers of Fear*, some of which show his characteristic cleverness. As a crime novelist, however, MacDonald's career really ended in the 'thirties. It is not surprising that he has been forgotten.

The exuberant and indefatigable American crime buff Dilys Winn recently discovered MacDonald living in the Motion Picture Retirement Home near Malibu, and talked to him about his career. She found him inclined to deprecate the books that had made his name: 'They're all a bit dated, aren't they?' *The*

Noose he thought 'awfully old-fashioned', and he would probably have said the same about *The Maze*. Dilys Winn found conversation difficult, and from her account of the interview one gets the impression that the time when MacDonald wrote crime stories was for him an ocean and a different life away. He belonged even in appearance to that different life. For the interview he sported an ascot, carried a silver-handled cane, and had his hair precisely parted and slicked down with pomade.

He said firmly that he was born in 1900, but this would mean that his first book *Ambrotox and Limping Dick*, written in collaboration with his father, was published when he was twenty years old. He thought that his best book was *Patrol*, which is not a crime story, rated his short stories higher than his novels, and expressed his aversion to literary company. 'Two writers in one room is too many.'

I think it must be acknowledged that *The Maze*, like its author, is a period piece, but it is one that must give pleasure to any reader who likes to solve a puzzle and to pit his own wits against those of the author's detective. And there is another reason why I hope that Philip MacDonald will be pleased to see the book republished. The most wistful thing he said in the course of the interview was that the Home's library did not contain 'one tiny word, not one, of mine.' At least *The Maze* can now find its proper place upon the shelves.

JULIAN SYMONS
1980

PREFACE

I HAVE given this book the subtitle of 'An Exercise in Detection'.

I have used the word 'exercise' deliberately; I mean it to be an exercise not only upon my part, but upon the part of any reader who may have the tenacity to get through it. In Parts Two, Three and Four of the book—the actual evidence of the witnesses upon the first time of their calling and the summing up of the Coroner—is contained all the information upon which Gethryn has to work. In other words, you, the reader, and he, the detective, are upon an equal footing. You know just as much as and no more than he knows. He knows just as much as and no more than you. He finds out: could you have found out without his help?

I should like to emphasise that although, for the sake of 'balance' and of avoiding tediousness, part of the evidence (that is, the re-examination and re-examination of the witnesses) has been omitted, none of this evidence was anything except repetitive. Gethryn, in fact, was not supplied with this repetitive evidence, as is shown by the note to him from Lucas. What Gethryn had is what you have. From what you have he made his deductions.

I have frequently been annoyed—as any reader of the analytical type of detective fiction must have been annoyed—by books in which the detective holds an unfair advantage over the reader in that he has opportunities which the reader cannot share. He may, for instance, in Chapter II 'dash up to London and spend two hours there.' And then the reader, not having been allowed to see what the detective did during those two hours in London, is at a disadvantage. Again, in Chapter XVII, the detective may suddenly, in a foully offhand and altogether offensive manner, 'pick some small object off the ground' which he puts in his

1

waistcoat pocket and doesn't say anything more about until Chapter XXIII, when it forms the basis upon which his whole case is founded. Again the reader has been subjected to the most dastardly unfair play!

In this book I have striven to be absolutely fair to the reader. There is *nothing*—nothing at all—for the detective that the reader has not had. More, the reader has had his information in exactly the same form as the detective—that is, the verbatim report of evidence and question.

This is a *fair* story. If you get the right answer—not merely a 'guessed' answer, but an answer for which you are prepared to put forward reasons—then you are as good at this job as A. R. Gethryn. If you don't, you are not. In either case I think you should be satisfied—unless, of course, you find the whole business too impossibly easy, in which case you ought—if you are not indeed already one—to become a really big noise at Scotland Yard.

PHILIP MACDONALD
1932

PART ONE

MY DEAR GETHRYN,

It is with a good deal of diffidence that I approach you, remembering our conversation before you left England for this holiday. You said that upon no account were you going to 'inaugurate, contemplate or elucidate crime or any minor or major misdemeanours!' You also said, I believe, that you were not going to read any English newspapers while you were out of England. Be that as it may, I *am* worrying you. I would like you to understand, however, that the fact that I am worrying you is due only partly to my own inclination. Charters himself, Pike and Jordan—and, this morning, even Bunter—have all brought pressure to bear upon me. I suggested to Charters that if he wanted to worry you he should do it himself. But he wasn't having any. And so, as usual, I'm left to do the dirty work. It may be very pleasant to be the First Commissioner of Police. It's certainly very pleasant to be an ordinary Police Constable. But who would be an Assistant Commissioner?

I feel that I'm taking an unconscionably long time to get down to brass tacks. That's probably due to the fact that I'm dictating this letter and also to the fact that I'm nervous about its reception when I remember my promise to you of a few weeks back. However, here goes:

Since you've been away there has happened—near Kensington Gore of all unlikely places!—a case which is the most extraordinary within my fairly long experience and also, I am told, within the thirty-five years' experience of old Jordan. Certainly in all my knowledge—official and private, actual and literary—there has never been anything quite like it.

In Kensington, on the night of the 11-12th July, a man

was killed. He met his death, abiding by all the canons of the best 'mystery fiction' in his study. It is certain beyond all possibility of doubt that he was murdered. It also seems certain beyond all possibility of doubt that he met his death at the hands of a person who was, for the time being at least, resident beneath his roof. There were, besides the murdered man, ten people sleeping in the house on the night of his death. One of them must surely have done it! But it has proved quite impossible for us to fix upon this one person. This doesn't look good for the police. Moreover, it is intensely annoying to any person of intelligence. Having been with the case since it began a few weeks ago—which seem like ten years—I can most earnestly vouch for this. I felt—and still feel—as I used to feel as a child when I went to Maskelyne and Cook's. I can still feel the appalling, stifling, impotent irritation of the Irish peasant priest faced with the question: 'If God is omnipotent, can He make a stone so heavy that He can't lift it?'

What we want you to do is to look at the papers we have on the case and just see if you can spot anything which we may have overlooked. I think it is hopeless. But I also think—knowing you as I do—that the chance is worth taking even at the risk of drawing down upon myself a sulphurous rebuke.

I had originally intended to write this letter and ask your permission to send you the papers (verbatim report of inquest, etc.). On maturer thought, however, I have decided to enclose copies of these herewith, for it has struck me that your answer to a request as to whether one might send papers would be useless, whereas your re-action to a bundle of papers might well be one of sufficient curiosity at least to make you read them through. And if you do read them through I am convinced that the sheer complexity of an apparently simple business will decoy you into spending thought upon it—and that, after all, is what we really want.

With all my respects to your wife and admiration to your small son,

Yours very sincerely,
E. Lucas

PART TWO

VERBATIM REPORT OF EVIDENCE GIVEN AT THE
CORONER'S INQUEST HELD UPON THE BODY OF
MAXWELL BRUNTON, DECEASED (1st DAY)

I

L.I. 84833 Sergeant George Crawley, Metropolitan Police

What is your full name?
George Crawley.
Now, will you please take the oath.
I swear by Almighty God that what I shall say in evidence in this Court shall be the truth, the whole truth, and nothing but the truth.
You are a sergeant in the Metropolitan Police Force?
Yes. L.I. 84833. Full-Sergeant George Crawley.
Would you please tell the Court, Sergeant, the circumstances under which you were called to 44 Rajah Gardens in the early morning of Thursday last, the twelfth of July.
I was going round the beats. I had just spoken to the constable in charge of the Baroness Gardens—Stukeley Road beat, and was walking on to my next point, going through the northern end of Rajah Gardens, when a man ran out of one of the houses and hailed me. Time 2.40 a.m. He told me he was a servant at Number 44, Mr Maxwell Brunton's. He was agitated and made a rambling statement which I had some difficulty in following. He was dressed in a dressing gown and slippers. On the doorstep there was a gentleman in evening dress. He said he was Mr Brunton's secretary, and he himself had just made the discovery that Mr Brunton was dead in his study. I asked to see the room, and this gentleman, Mr Harrison, said he would take me up. There were a number of the other inmates of the house gathered round in the hall. I asked them to stay where they were until sent for. I also sent the manservant, Jennings, to fetch the constable on the beat and told him to let me know when he arrived.

11

I then mounted the stairs with Mr Harrison, who took me to the deceased's study. This is a room at the western side of the house. It is a room which has been built out over the area which lies below, beside the passage leading through from the street to the gardens belonging to the block. There is only one door to this study. This door faces you as you go down the corridor after turning left from the landing . . .

One moment, Sergeant. Have the police any plans of this house? Perhaps the jury might like to see them.

Yes, sir. One was put in with the other Police papers. I think it was marked Number 6 on the docket.

Ah! . . . Number 6 you said. Yes! Yes! Stupid of me . . . Gentlemen, you may like to pass this plan round among yourselves.

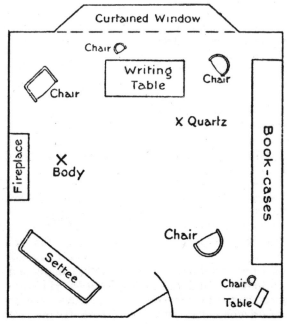

Plan of study at 44 Rajah Gardens.

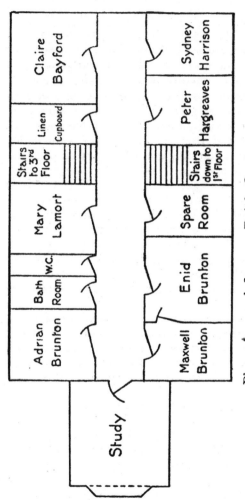

Plan of second floor 44 Rajah Gardens.

.   .   .   .   .   .

Thank you. I hope the plan is clear to you all.

.   .   .   .   .   .

Excellent! Now, Sergeant, if you'll continue . . .

Very good, sir. I entered the study and found the body of the deceased lying on the hearth-rug. With the police papers, sir, there's a plan of the room showing the exact position of the body. The head was pointing toward the centre of the bay window and the feet toward the door. Deceased was dead. I judged life to have been extinct for quite a while. The only injury I could find on examination was to the right eye. This had been penetrated, the object which effected the injury having pierced apparently right through to the brain. There was a good deal of blood. Lying by the body was a large lump of mineral which I took to be gold quartz. That mineral lump is among your exhibits, sir. I found the long spur which projects from one end of it to be covered with blood. The lump was lying at some distance from the body at the spot marked Q on the plan which you will see is close by the foot of the writing-table. There were no signs of struggle or any disturbance in the room. All the furniture, papers, etc., on the desk were quite tidy.

I made a rapid plan of the room and then went downstairs again with Mr Harrison, locking the door and retaining the key.

One moment, Sergeant. Did you examine the windows of the study?

Yes, sir. They were all open. You will remember it had been a hot night, sir. I examined the windows particularly with a view to ascertaining whether it would have been possible for anyone to leave the room by that means. In my opinion, sir, such a thing was impossible. The room is on the second story of the house, and being built on extra, as it has, there is simply a clean drop down to the back area of the kitchen. There is nothing on the wall for foot or hand-hold. There are no trees near by, and there is nothing near the windows inside the room which could have been used to sling a rope round.

I see. Thank you, Sergeant. You were saying that you went downstairs with Mr Harrison.

Yes, sir. When we got to the foot of the stairs I found that the manservant had returned with a constable. I placed the constable on duty outside the door and then telephoned to my headquarters and reported. I was given instructions to take preliminary statements from the members of the house, and did so. Those statements are, I believe, together with the other statements taken later, in the police papers which you have got, sir.

I see . . . Now, Sergeant, one or two questions. You were the first outside person to enter this house, and your impressions may be of value. Can you tell us how the different members of the family seemed to be reacting to the discovery of Mr Brunton's death? In what order did you see them?

Mr Harrison first, sir, then Mrs Brunton, then Mr Adrian Brunton, then Mrs Bayford, the deceased's sister, then Mr Hargreaves, a visitor. That was all, sir. I couldn't take any statement from the other visitor, Miss Lamort, because she wasn't in a fit state. The five persons I've just mentioned, sir, they were all very quiet, as you might say. Seemed more stunned than anything else, though all answered the questions I put to them without hesitation.

You say, Sergeant, that Miss Lamort was so much agitated that she could not be questioned. What was she doing? Was she fainting? Or in hysterics? Or in a state of collapse?

I should say a state of collapse, sir. Miss Lamort was not one of those persons in the hall when I first entered the house. She was not in the hall when I came downstairs after examining the study. What happened was this: I looked round and then I asked Mr Harrison—he seemed the most collected of those persons—I asked Mr Harrison whether everyone was there. He then told me that there were three inmates of the house presumably still in their bedrooms—the kitchenmaid Violet Burrage, Mrs Brunton's maid Jinette Bokay, and Miss Lamort. I left the constable in charge downstairs and went up with Mr Harrison to rouse these three persons. The girl Burrage was fast asleep; we had to enter her room and wake her, and it took us quite a time. The young woman Bokay was already awake—she said the disturbance in the house had roused her. She was beginning to dress when we got there and seemed very scared. Those two rooms were in the top or attic story of the house, as you will see from the plan. It's up there that all the servants sleep. We then came downstairs, and Mr Harrison took me to Miss Lamort's room. There was a light shining under the door. The door was locked. Mr Harrison and I both took turns at knocking but could not get any reply for quite a while. At last we heard Miss Lamort's voice asking, 'Who's there? Who's there?' Mr Harrison answered. He explained that there had been an accident and that everybody was wanted. We heard Miss Lamort getting out of bed. She came to the door at once and opened it. When she saw my uniform she seemed to stagger. She nearly fell, only Mr Harrison caught her in time. She said: 'What's happened? What's happened?' Mr Harrison told her that there had been an accident and that Mr Brunton was dead and that naturally the police had to make a few inquiries. She then said: 'I must get some clothes on. I'll come down.' I waited. In a very short time she came to the door again, dressed, and I asked her to accompany me downstairs.

In the hall she rushed to Mrs Brunton and caught hold of her and seemed to break down properly. Mrs Brunton and Mrs Bayford tried to soothe her. I gave them permission to take her into the library, which opens just off the hall, so that she could lie down. I then entered the dining-room and began to call in the persons one by one. When I'd questioned Mr Harrison, Mrs Brunton and Mrs Bayford, Mr Adrian Brunton and Mr Hargreaves, I wanted to question Miss Lamort. I went into the library and found her. She was lying on the sofa. She was very pale and didn't seem to appreciate what was going on.

Detective Inspector Syme then arrived with the divisional surgeon and took charge.

Thank you, Sergeant . . . Are there any further questions which the jury would wish to put to this witness at this stage? . . . No? . . . Very well. Thank you, Sergeant; you may stand down . . . Call Inspector Syme.

II

DETECTIVE INSPECTOR JOHN SYME

WHAT is your full name?

John Syme.

Will you please take the oath?

I swear by Almighty God that what I shall say in evidence in this Court shall be the truth, the whole truth and nothing but the truth.

You are a member of the Metropolitan Police Force?

Yes. I am a Detective Inspector of L.I. Division.

Will you please tell the Court, Inspector Syme, the circumstances under which you were called to 44 Rajah Gardens on the morning of Thursday, 12th July?

I was called on the telephone by Sergeant Crawley at 2.55 a.m. on Thursday last. Sergeant Crawley reported that there was a death at 44 Rajah Gardens, the deceased being Maxwell Brunton, the leaseholder of the house. Sergeant Crawley stated that the circumstances of the death were indicative of murder. I immediately called a car and fetched the Divisional Surgeon, Dr Crosby, and I then proceeded at once with him to 44 Rajah Gardens, reaching there at 3.12 a.m.

You heard Sergeant Crawley's evidence, Inspector Syme?

Yes.

When you entered the house I assume that you went to the study and inspected the body?

Yes. I found everything as described by Sergeant Crawley and as shown on the plan which you have before you.

Were you able, Inspector, to form any theory as to whether death was caused by the deceased himself, by accident, or by some other person or persons?

I came to the definite conclusion that death could not have been caused either accidentally or by the deceased himself.

Will you please tell the Court, in your own words, Inspector Syme, what you did after your inspection of the study?

I followed the usual routine. I took official charge of the premises, put a constable on duty outside the study, sent for the Police photographers and notified the Divisional Chief Inspector, who asked me to notify Scotland Yard, which I did. I then questioned the inmates of the house. The statements made by them, both to Sergeant Crawley and myself, are with the Police papers which you have before you.

One more question, Inspector. I realise that it is unnecessary for us to get you to inform the Court as to the substance of the statements which you obtained from the members of the household since the gentlemen of the Jury have these statements before them, and, further, will hear the persons themselves giving evidence in due course. But I should like you to tell the Court in what state you found the various inmates when you did question them . . . We must bear in mind, gentlemen, that when Inspector Syme arrived he had his investigations to make of the scene of death and various other official duties to perform before he entered upon his questioning, and that, therefore, some considerable time would have elapsed between the time of the first questioning by Sergeant Crawley and the second questioning by Inspector Syme . . . How long would you say that time was, Inspector?

I should say roughly three-quarters of an hour.

Thank you. Now, if you would go on to answer my main question?

I saw the witnesses in the following order: Mrs Brunton, Mr Adrian Brunton, Mrs Bayford, Mr Harrison, Mr Hargreaves, Miss Lamort, Arthur Jennings, the butler, Mrs Jennings, his wife, Jeannette Bocquet, Mrs Brunton's maid, and Violet Burrage, the kitchenmaid. Mrs Brunton, though much distressed, was quite lucid in her answers. Mr Adrian Brunton was lucid enough but in a nervous state which had reacted unfavourably upon his temper. Mr Harrison was nervous and slightly confused and only made himself clear with some difficulty. Mrs Bayford was suffering from severe shock and could only answer questions. She did not seem able to make any voluntary statement. Mr Hargreaves's behaviour seemed normal. Miss Lamort was in an extreme state of collapse. I could not ask her as many questions as I should have wished, as, shortly after my arrival, I found that her medical adviser, Dr Fothergill, had been summoned. When he came he advised me that it would not be well to continue with any attempt to question Miss Lamort that night. Accordingly I got her full statement, which you have before you, the next day. In regard to the servants, Arthur Jennings and Mrs Jennings were normal. Burrage seemed half stupefied by shock and Jeanette Bocquet highly excited.

Thank you, Inspector. Now, another point, and a very important one. It is, I know, dealt with in the Police papers which we have, but I think should also be discussed in Court. Was there any indication that No. 44 Rajah Gardens had been entered by any person other than the inmates during the night?

No indication whatsoever.

In your opinion, Inspector, would it have been possible for any other person to have entered the house, make their way to the study and then leave the house?

I am satisfied that such an entry would have been impossible; impossible, that is, without the assistance of some person or persons within the house.

Upon what grounds, Inspector, do you base your certainty upon this point?

The front door was bolted by Jennings as early as 10.15 p.m.—a fact to which various witnesses testify. The windows on the ground floor were also locked and shuttered immediately afterwards—a fact also testified to. The basement windows and door were locked and bolted as usual by Mrs Jennings and Violet Burrage at 9.30 p.m. The construction and position of the house make it entirely improbable—in fact, sir, impossible—

for anyone to obtain access to them without the use of ladders. Certainly no entrance could be made through any window without traces being left, and there were no traces. In regard to the study windows, as Sergeant Crawley stated in his evidence, the idea of entrance and exit through them need not be entertained.

Thank you, Inspector . . . I don't think we need trouble Inspector Syme any further—at this stage, anyhow . . .

Call Dr Richard Crosby.

III

James Richard Crosby, M.R.C.S., L.R.C.P., Private Practice and Divisional Surgeon L.I. Division, Metropolitan Police.

What is your full name?

James Richard Crosby.

Now will you take the oath?

I swear by Almighty God that what I shall say in evidence in this Court shall be the truth, the whole truth and nothing but the truth.

You act, I believe, in the capacity of Divisional Surgeon to L.I. Division of the Metropolitan Police?

Yes.

Will you please describe to the Court, Dr Crosby, your visit to 44 Rajah Gardens in the early morning of Thursday last?

I was called out at 3.5 a.m. I went with Detective Inspector Syme of the Division to Number 44 Rajah Gardens. I was taken to the study and there found and examined the body of the deceased. I found death to have been caused by a blow which had pierced through the cavity of the right eye into the brain. Internal hæmorrhage had immediately set in; death must have taken place within a very short time after the blow was received. I was then shown a large lump of mineral quartz which had projecting from it at one end a long jagged spur. The end of this spur was caked with blood and tissue. I formed the opinion that it was beyond doubt this lump of quartz which had been the weapon causing death.

It was, I understand, approximately 3.30 a.m. when you examined the body?

That is correct.

In your opinion, how long had life been extinct?

Not more than six hours had elapsed since death had transpired.

Doctor, in your examination of the body, did you form any opinion as to the deceased's general health?

I should say it was very good. Magnificent development. Obviously kept himself in very good condition. More like, in fact, the body of a man of forty than fifty-five, which I believe is what he was.

Did you form any opinion, Doctor, as to how the wound might have been caused?

Yes. With, as I have said, the quartz. A strong, stabbing blow was probably struck.

Is it at all possible, Doctor, that the wound was self-inflicted?

In my opinion, absolutely impossible.

I do not think there are any other questions, gentlemen? . . . No? . . . Thank you, Doctor. That is all.

Call Sidney Harrison.

IV

Sidney Foljambe Harrison, Private Secretary to the Deceased

What is your full name?

Sidney Foljambe Harrison.

Will you please take the oath?

I swear by Almighty God that what I shall say in evidence in this Court shall be the truth, the whole truth and nothing but the truth.

You were, I believe, private secretary to the deceased?

Private and *confidential* secretary. I was secretary to Mr Brunton for a considerable period, over which he and I got to know each other, if I may say so, extremely well. I was fully conversant with Mr Brunton's—

One moment, Mr Harrison. I should be glad if, at this stage of your evidence, you would confine yourself to answering my questions.

Certainly, certainly. I have no wish to be of anything but assistance.

Quite! . . . Perhaps you would tell me, Mr Harrison, how long you held the position of secretary to the deceased?

I was private and confidential secretary to Mr Maxwell Brunton for eleven months. That is, to be precise, Mr Coroner, I should have completed my year upon the fifth of next month. If I may say so, the eleven months were—

Thank you. Will you please inform the Court of the time at which you last saw your employer alive?

Certainly I will. Let me see . . . I was with the rest of the household—excepting, of course, the servants—in the drawing-room after dinner. We had all been in the room for the whole of the time since dinner . . . There had been bridge—

One moment.—Do I understand you to say, Mr Harrison, that everyone in the house was in the drawing-room after dinner, excepting the servants?

No, no, no! Everyone with the exception of Mr Maxwell Brunton himself.

Thank you. Please continue.

At 11 p.m. exactly—I happened to just have looked at my watch—Mr Maxwell Brunton, who had retired to his study (to work, he said) immediately after dinner, came down and joined the party. He chatted a few moments and then bade everyone good-night, saying that he would be working late and telling me, incidentally, that he would not require my services. When he left the drawing-room—the last time I saw him alive—the time would be, I should say, about five minutes past eleven; perhaps a little more.

Now, Mr Harrison, will you please describe to the Court your discovery of Mr Brunton's body?

Yes. At 2.30 a.m. on Friday morning it suddenly occurred to me that there was an important engagement which I had omitted to note on Mr Brunton's desk pad. I was at that time, of course, in my bedroom, but I was not in bed. I was studying, as I commonly do, until the very early hours. I do not believe in putting things off, and so I decided to go along to the study and remedy my error without delay.

My bedroom is on the same floor: that is, the second. I accordingly walked softly along the passage, being very careful to make no noise at so late an hour. I did not switch on the passage light, as I know my way so well. I was therefore in the dark, and I saw, as I approached, a light beneath the study door. I assumed that Mr Brunton might be engaged and so knocked upon the door before entering. No reply came to my first knock or to my second. Not wishing to disturb the house, I did not knock again but softly turned the handle. I then made the shocking discovery.

The body, as the sergeant described, was lying on the

hearth-rug. The head was pointing toward the window, and the feet toward the door. I was, as you may imagine, horrified and aghast, but I flatter myself that I wasted no time. It needed no expert eye to see that Mr Brunton was dead. I went quietly out of the study, shutting the door behind me; ran as fast as my legs would carry me back to the stairs and up to the top floor and waked Jennings the butler. In a few words I told him what had happened and sent him out for a policeman. The disturbance had apparently wakened Mrs Brunton, for as I came downstairs after Jennings she was on the landing. I had to break the news to her, and she insisted that I should rouse—er—bring to her her son and daughter, Mr Adrian Brunton and Mrs Bayford. I called Mr Adrian Brunton. Mrs Bayford, taking matters into her own hands, called Mr Hargreaves, who was staying in the house. Sarah Jennings, wakened when I called her husband, came downstairs. Mr Adrian Brunton and Mrs Brunton wished to go at once to the study, but I managed to dissuade them from taking this step until after the police had arrived. I was seconded in this by Mr Hargreaves.

We all went downstairs to the hall. All the members of the household, that is to say with the exception of the kitchenmaid, Mrs Brunton's maid and Miss Lamort, the third visitor. We had not been downstairs more than a moment when Jennings came back with the sergeant. After that events transpired as he told you in his evidence.

I trust, Mr Coroner, that I have been clear in my statement. I try always to make a habit of orderly and incisive thinking.

Yes, yes, quite. Now, Mr Harrison, one or two questions . . .

At your service, Mr Coroner.

When you were describing just now how at Mrs Brunton's request you fetched her son and daughter, you started to use the word 'rouse' and then apparently changed your mind.

Exactly, Mr Coroner. I felt, as I said it, that perhaps 'rouse' was not the correct word. It might imply that Mrs Bayford and Mr Adrian Brunton were asleep, whereas in fact they were not.

Did you enter their rooms?

Mr Brunton's, yes. I gave one tap at the door and entered rather unceremoniously. Mr Brunton was kneeling upon the window seat looking out of the window. He had a dressing-gown on but had only substituted this, I saw, for his dinner jacket.

What did he do when you came in? Can you tell the Court his reaction to your entry and your bad news?

Certainly. When I went in—as I have said, rather unceremoniously, I fear—Mr Brunton got up and turned round to face me. Before I could speak he said: 'What the hell do *you* want?' I should perhaps explain that Mr Brunton has always seemed—for what reason I am sure I cannot think—to dislike me.

Did he seem excited when he said this?

A difficult question, Mr Coroner. Mr Adrian Brunton is a young man of—er—mercurial temperament. He is normally excitable. It certainly did not strike me that there was anything unusual—for him—in his reception of me, though naturally I resented his incivility.

You say Mr Brunton was looking out of his window? If my recollection of the plan is correct, this would mean that he was looking out over the gardens to Rajah Square—

That is correct. Mr Adrian Brunton's room is at the back of the house; that is, the northern side—

Please let me conclude my question before answering, Mr Harrison. I was about to ask you if you gathered from Mr Adrian Brunton's position as you entered the room any indication of whether he was merely idly looking out into the gardens or looking out for, or at, any particular object?

I am afraid it is impossible for me to say. No sooner had I entered the room than he was off the window seat and had turned to face me.

Thank you. Please proceed. You were about to tell the Court in answer to my question what Mr Brunton's reaction was to your bad news?

He seemed dazed. In fact, for a moment I wondered whether

he had heard me. I said 'Don't you understand, Mr Brunton? Your father is dead—has been killed! . . .'

Yes, Mr Harrison? Please don't hesitate. What then?

I suppose that in this Court I must repeat the exact words which were used. After I had told him a second time Mr Brunton caught me by the shoulder and shook me violently. He said: 'You bloody little bastard! That's a lie!' I managed not to allow my very natural resentment to overcome my good sense. I managed to make Mr Brunton understand that I was in deadly earnest. He then put out his arm and brushed me aside. I followed him out into the corridor. He had opened the study door, which of course was just at his right as he came out of his own room, and was standing on the threshold, staring. I said: 'Mr Brunton! Mr Brunton! We must leave things as they are until the Police come.' He muttered some oath or other which I did not catch and I think was going into the study, but at that moment he heard Mrs Brunton's voice calling him from the other end of the corridor. She was just outside Mrs Bayford's room. He turned and ran back. I followed.

As I passed the stairhead Mrs Bayford came out of her room. I think she was following her mother. She was fully dressed, but not in the gown which she had worn at dinner. I remember she had in her hand a fountain pen, because I offered to take it from her and put it down. She had obviously already heard the news. She stared at me as though I were not there. I repeated my offer, but she turned away without a word and began speaking with her brother.

So you are not in a position, Mr Harrison, to tell us Mrs Bayford's immediate reaction to her father's death?

No, sir. As I was breaking the dreadful news to Mr Adrian Brunton, Mrs Brunton must have been with her daughter.

I see. Now, you say that when you did see Mrs Bayford—when she came out of her room—and you and Mr Brunton and Mrs Brunton were standing in the corridor, she seemed dazed when you spoke to her?

I did not use the word 'dazed,' Mr Coroner. Mrs Bayford certainly was not in a normal state, for, as a rule, she is a lady of most charming manner, and, as I have explained, she did not seem to hear my offer of assistance. But although she was not herself, I do not think it would be right for me to use the word 'dazed.' She seemed in a way peculiarly alert. It was she, for instance, who called Mr Hargreaves, outside whose room we all were standing at the moment. She rapped on the door, and it was immediately opened. Mr Hargreaves was in pyjamas and a dressing-gown. From his appearance I should say that he had been in bed. The terrible situation was explained to him, and it was after that that we—

One moment, Mr Harrison, one moment! Please tell the Court who it was who conveyed the news to Mr Hargreaves.

Mrs Bayford. I can remember her exact words, I think, Mr Coroner. She laid her hand on Mr Hargreaves's arm, and she said: 'Oh, Jack dear! A frightful thing has happened ... Father—Father—' and then she seemed to break down for a moment. Mr Hargreaves caught her hands, and he said: 'Claire! Claire! What's this?' or some words like that. And then Mrs Bayford seemed to take command of herself again. She said, 'Father's dead. He's been ... he's been killed.' And it was after that that we all—

One moment, Mr Harrison! It's very important that the Court should appreciate the relationship in which the persons staying at the house stood to each other. It is also very important that you should tell us, as much as you can, of each person's reaction on their hearing the news. Will you please tell us, first, of Mr Hargreaves's demeanour when Mrs Bayford had explained the tragedy to him, and secondly, what you know of the relationship between these two. I understood you to say that Mrs Bayford called Mr Hargreaves 'Jack dear,' and that he in return used her Christian name.

To take your first question, Mr Coroner, Mr Hargreaves, on hearing the dreadful news, seemed—and quite naturally—utterly astonished. He made some ejaculation—'Good God!' I think it was—but when this astonishment had passed he seemed mostly concerned with the effect of the tragedy upon Mrs Bayford.

In answer to your second question, Mr Coroner, I can only say that, not being a member of the family, and, as Mr Brunton's secretary, naturally not being in the confidence of any of the rest of the family, I can only give you my own, as it were, casual impressions. I have always understood that Mr Hargreaves is an old friend of Mrs Bayford; and this visit was the first time I had ever come into personal contact with Mr Hargreaves, but I had frequently heard mention of him. I have always understood that Mr Hargreaves and Mrs Bayford knew each other from childhood right up to the time when Mrs Bayford married, two years ago, but that after that Mr Hargreaves went abroad. I believe he only returned a little while ago.

I see. You cannot tell us, I suppose, whether there had ever been any talk of a marriage between Mrs Bayford and Mr Hargreaves?

I have no information upon that point, Mr Coroner. Such matters are not any business of mine, and I am afraid that I make a strict rule of never prying into matters which do not concern me.

Most commendable, I'm sure! Can you tell the Court anything of the relations between Mr Hargreaves and the rest of the family?

There, sir, I may be of a little more use. Three days before his death Mr Maxwell Brunton referred in my presence to the forthcoming visit of Mr Hargreaves. He came into the study where I was working on his letters and asked me to cancel an appointment he had made for dinner on the Thursday night. From the way in which he worded his directions I gathered that he was not looking forward with any degree of pleasure to Mr Hargreaves's visit. So far as the other members of the family are—

Just one moment, Mr Harrison! Can you remember the exact words used by Mr Maxwell Brunton in regard to Mr Hargreaves on this occasion you have just told us of?

Mr Brunton made no direct reference to Mr Hargreaves personally, but he said—I'm afraid I cannot remember the exact words—something like this: 'That'll be young Hargreaves's first night here. Blast it!' And then later, discussing some appointment for the Saturday he said again: 'Hargreaves will still be here. Damn it!' or some words like that . . . What I am trying to show, Mr Coroner, is that while Mr Brunton did not make any ill-natured reference to Mr Hargreaves personally, he did seem to find the forthcoming visit of Mr Hargreaves far from—how shall I put it?—far more awkward than he would have a visit of any other person. He was not a man who was given to being put out merely by the presence of an extra person in the house.

I see . . . Have you any further questions, gentlemen, that you would like me to put to this witness at this stage? . . . I beg your pardon? . . . Perhaps, sir, if you would get the foreman to put the question formally . . .

Mr Coroner, a member of the jury wishes me to ask whether the witness has any comment to offer on the evidence of the police sergeant or any addition to that evidence in regard to the other guest, Miss Lamort, and her collapse on hearing the news of deceased's death.

I see. Mr Harrison, you heard the foreman, I think. Perhaps you would give a reply to that question.

I have nothing to add, sir, to the police sergeant's remarks. I went, as described by the police sergeant, with him to wake Miss Lamort. As he stated, when we told her the news she seemed extremely agitated. During the very few moments she took to attire herself I kept hearing her mutter—we had not quite closed the door—'My God! My God!' This was said in a kind of moaning voice, very distressing to hear. When Miss Lamort came downstairs and rushed to Mrs Brunton for comfort, she seemed to collapse completely. She seemed terribly upset. She seemed not to take the news of the calamity nearly so stoically as the members of Mr Brunton's family. I should perhaps add that throughout the whole of the following day she was confined to her room, during which time she was, so the servants inform me, unable to take any food. I went once or twice myself past her room on that day, and each time I could hear her moaning and muttering words which I could not catch, as I was, of course, merely passing her door about my business ... There is no doubt that the tragedy affected her very, very deeply.

I see. Thank you, Mr Harrison. I was going to ask you to stand down just before the jury put that last question to you. Looking down my notes, however, I find there is one further question which I myself wish to put. I'm sorry to keep you so long.

Not at all! Not at all! I am here to do my duty.

Quite! Quite! The last question is this: Was it your habit, as confidential private secretary to Mr Brunton, always to knock at the study door if you thought he was inside the study?

Certainly not, sir! The study was my place of work, and anyhow, if I may say so, it is only household servants who are required to knock at such doors before entering.

And yet, Mr Harrison, during your evidence you made the following statement: you had just said that on your way to the study on Thursday night, or, rather, Friday morning, you saw a light beneath the study door, and then you added, 'I assumed that Mr Brunton was engaged and so knocked at the door before entering.' Will you please explain this seeming contradiction to what you have just told the Court?

You put me in a truly embarrassing position, Mr Coroner. I come up here and strive to the best of my ability to give my evidence simply, concisely and above all, truthfully—

Quite, quite! Will you please answer the question? Is the Court to take it that you assume that your employer would not like you to go in at such a time as that without knocking?

If you insist upon my answering that question, Mr Coroner, yes.

You are here to answer questions, Mr Harrison. Will you

please now tell the Court the reason for supposing that Mr Brunton would like warning of your entry?

I must answer that question?

Of course. May I suggest, Mr Harrison, that you do not waste our time and your own? So far you have shown no disinclination either to answer questions or to add your own quota to your answers. May I suggest that you continue in this manner?

Very well, sir. Since you insist—since you insist, I say—upon an answer to this question of yours, I am in duty bound to give you an answer. I knocked upon Mr Brunton's study door because I thought Mr Brunton might not be alone.

And yet, although your errand to the study was only a question of making a diary entry which you had forgotten, you did not, when you saw the light and thought that Mr Brunton might be engaged, go away again without making your presence known?

Really, Mr Coroner, I must take leave to know my own business best! I gave every satisfaction to Mr Brunton—the length of my sojourn with him is enough guarantee of that. I trust that I know my position and what, in that position, I may or may not do. I thought Mr Brunton might be engaged, but, equally, it was possible that he was only, as he very often was until very early hours, reading or writing.

Quite! Quite! Who, Mr Harrison, did you think might be engaged with Mr Brunton? His son? His wife? His daughter?

I am afraid, Mr Coroner, that such conjectures did not enter my head. I am a man who makes a practice of never concerning himself unduly with the private affairs of others, especially those of the employer to whom he owes loyalty.

You had no idea, then, Mr Harrison, of who might be with Mr Brunton? You did not, for instance, listen a moment to see . . . Please do not misunderstand me. I am not making a suggestion of eavesdropping. You did not, I suppose, listen for a moment to hear if there were voices, or whether you could distinguish those voices?

Most emphatically not, sir!

Thank you.

I would like to say at this juncture—

Please do not trouble, Mr Harrison. I think I can now ask you to stand down—that is, of course, unless any member of the jury has any further questions which he wishes to put to you . . . I beg your pardon? . . . Please speak up . . .

Mr Harrison, I'm not sure whether you heard the question of the jury. They wish to know whether, when you knocked, you expected the person who might be engaged with Mr Brunton to be a man or a woman?

Really, Mr Coroner! I am afraid I am not familiar with this kind of procedure, but I cannot think that it is customary or permissible to—

Mr Harrison, I wish you would get it into your head that this is a court of inquiry. The object of the inquiry is to ascertain how Mr Maxwell Brunton met his death. Petty private feelings and even the ordinary social shibboleths are out of place. When, as a witness, you are asked a question, it is your duty to answer that question as succinctly as you can. I will repeat it in another form: When you knocked on the study door because you thought Mr Maxwell Brunton was 'engaged,' did any thought cross your mind as to the sex of his possible companion? Now, please, Mr Harrison, we don't want your opinion; we want your answer.

Yes, Mr Coroner. I thought that Mr Brunton might have—might have—er—a lady with him.

What lady? Mrs Brunton? Please confine yourself solely to answering my question.

No, not Mrs Brunton. Mrs Brunton is—er—Mrs Brunton hardly ever went into the study.

Who then?

I cannot say, Mr Coroner.

Do you mean 'can not' or 'will not'?

I am not in the habit, Mr Coroner, of using a word in its wrong place. If I say 'cannot,' I mean I am unable.

So you intend to inform the Court, first, that you did not think this possible visitor of Mr Brunton's could be Mrs Brunton, and, second, that it might be any other person of the female sex?

.   .   .   .   .   .

Come, come, Mr Harrison! Please give us your answer!

As you insist, Mr Coroner, yes.

Do you mean to tell the Court that you thought it possible that a woman other than one of those in the house could be with Mr Brunton?

Good heavens, no! What are you suggesting?

Please spare us your indignation, Mr Harrison. If you did not think, then, that this possible visitor could be a woman from outside, and yet you thought that it was a woman, will you please tell the Court which female member of the household you thought most likely—

Really, Mr Coroner, I cannot—

Please, Mr Harrison! You must remember, sir, if you are at all uncomfortable, that, really, you have brought this upon yourself. Please give an answer to my question. I gather from the general trend of your evidence that the possible woman was not Mrs Brunton nor Mrs Bayford. That leaves us, I think, with Miss Lamort and the servants, Mrs Jennings, Jeannette Bokay, and Violet Burrage—

Really, Mr Coroner! I must emphatically state at this point that any conjectures I may have had on the subject did not go so far as the identity of the possible person.

You are certain of that, Mr Harrison?

Positive, sir! Positive!

Very well, Mr Harrison. We will now cease, I hope, to embarrass you. You were Mr Brunton's confidential secretary. You must therefore have had manifold opportunities for observing Mr Brunton's temperament, character, and ways. That is so?

Obviously, sir.

Very well, then! Perhaps you would tell the Court whether you had noticed anything unusual in Mr Maxwell Brunton's demeanour at any time, say, within the month preceding his death.

Emphatically, no, Mr Coroner. Mr Brunton was always a volatile personality. He was, if you take my meaning, gay one moment and dour the next. But I knew him very well, and a more generous, more understanding or more considerate employer one could not wish for. I was with Mr Brunton for a considerable period . . .

Yes, yes! Please will you confine yourself to answering the question? Are we to understand that you had noticed nothing unusual in Mr Brunton's behaviour at any time immediately prior to his death?

You are, sir.

There was no depression, then? No fear, no private or public trouble which Mr Brunton told you about or which you got to know of in any way?

Until the day of his death, no, sir. And, I suppose, really nothing outstanding upon that day. You have cautioned me, Mr Coroner, because you appear to think that I give unduly long and inapposite answers, and therefore I had better perhaps confine myself to stating that—

Come, come! Please! Are we to gather that there was some unusual depression on the part of Mr Brunton on the day of his death, or some unusual and unpleasant happening?

I was striving, Mr Coroner, to answer your question to the best of my ability. I do not want to exaggerate any of the matters or to minimise them. I simply seek to do my duty. On the day of his death Mr Brunton *was* worried. I am afraid that I am cognisant of the cause of this worry—perhaps I should use the plural because it was worries and not worry. On that day it came to my knowledge that Mr Brunton had various—er—how shall I put it?—disagreements with members of his family. Nothing serious, of course, and really, if you had not asked such specific questions, I should not have thought these things worth mentioning.

With whom were these disagreements, Mr Harrison?

Perhaps, Mr Coroner, 'disagreements' was too strong a word,

and really, you know, I cannot see that mere family breezes, shall I say, can have—

Mr Harrison! What you can or cannot see is no doubt interesting. The Court, however, merely wishes for facts. With whom, to your knowledge, did Mr Brunton, upon the day preceding the morning of his death, have these disagreements?

There was one small disagreement, Mr Coroner, with Mrs Brunton, and another with Mr Adrian Brunton.

When did the disagreement with Mrs Brunton take place?

It was hardly a disagreement—I beg your pardon, Mr Coroner—I will confine myself to facts. At about eleven o'clock in the morning Mrs Brunton—a most unusual thing for her—came to the study. She stated that she wished to speak to Mr Brunton privately, and of course I immediately left the room. As I did so Mr Brunton called after me, 'We must get that McGuinness affair settled, Harrison. Come back in ten minutes.' I returned after ten minutes. Mrs Brunton, as I got to the door, was just coming out of it. I noticed that she had—that she had been shedding a few tears. Mr Brunton was walking up and down with his hands behind his back. He was—a trick of his when disturbed—muttering indistinguishably to himself. However, immediately he caught sight of me he became his old self, and we proceeded with our work.

That was the first little affair. The second—Mr Adrian Brunton's—took place in the afternoon. I had been out for my constitutional, and I came back as usual about three-thirty. I had understood that Mr Brunton was not to be at home that afternoon, and naturally I went, after I had put up my hat and stick, straight to the study. As I drew near the door I became aware that Mr Brunton had not gone out after all. I heard his voice raised, apparently in anger. I hesitated a moment, not quite knowing whether I should go forward or tactfully retire. As I was, in fact, retiring, I heard another voice which I knew for Mr Adrian Brunton's. That, too, was raised. It was even louder than Mr Brunton's. It was uttering violent remarks of some description. Of course, I beat a very hasty retreat in order that I should not even inadvertently overhear anything not intended for my ears.

I see. Then you can give the Court no idea, Mr Harrison, of what either of the disputants were saying?

No idea whatever, Mr Coroner. As I came to the door and heard Mr Maxwell Brunton speaking, I did catch the words 'not if you and your mother *and* that little—er, ahem!—bitch came to me on your bended knees,' and then, as I was hastily retiring, I caught one or two words of Mr Adrian Brunton. He seemed to be—he is, I fear, as excitable or even more so than his father—using many violent epithets. The only remark of his which I clearly caught—you must remember, sir, that I was endeavouring not to hear, rather than to hear—the only remark which I clearly caught was something like 'Bloody nice sort of father! You can have all your little bits, but when it comes to your son wanting to settle down . . .' After that, Mr Coroner, I heard nothing. I was, you must understand—

Yes. Yes. Quite! You're sure of these speeches, Mr Harrison?

Certainly, sir. I never say anything of which I am not sure.

I see. I asked you because they seemed rather lengthy to have been heard during this very brief sojourn of yours outside the study door. Nevertheless, I take it that you would swear to them?

Most emphatically, sir—and I must say that I fail to—

Shall we leave it at that, Mr Harrison? I would now like to ask you whether such family disturbances were usual in the Brunton household?

I find that a very difficult question to answer, sir. You must understand that not being a member of the family and being one who makes a point of never, shall we say, prying into other people's affairs, and especially his employer's—

I was asking you, Mr Harrison, whether such quarrels were usual in the Brunton household, to your knowledge.

So far as I am concerned, Mr Coroner, they were neither more usual nor more unusual than in any other household with which I have ever been associated. Mr Adrian Brunton, of course, has inherited his father's volatile temperament, and they certainly were quite frequently at loggerheads about this and that. Mrs Brunton and Mr Maxwell Brunton were, however, an ideal pair. I think this occasion was the only one upon which I have noticed that there had been even any slight trouble between them. Mr Brunton, of course, was a man of very great energy, both mentally and physically, and he was always so busy with both his City work and his writing work and his numerous—er—hobbies, that he really seemed to see very little of Mrs Brunton, but I must say, however, that his manner toward her always showed respect and affection.

Very well. Gentlemen, if you have no further questions to ask this witness at the present stage . . .? Personally, I recommend that we should proceed to take the evidence of the other witnesses. Mr Harrison will be available if we need him later. Is that agreed? . . . Thank you, Mr Harrison. You may stand down. We may want you later.

Call Arthur Waterloo Jennings.

V

ARTHUR WATERLOO JENNINGS, BUTLER AND PARLOURMAN TO MAXWELL BRUNTON, DECEASED

WHAT is your full name?

Arthur Waterloo Jennings.

Please keep silence in the Court! . . . Now, Jennings, will you please take the oath.

With all me 'eart, sir! I swear by Almighty God that what I shall say in this Court—

One moment, Jennings, one moment! Will you please hold the Book? . . . Give him the Book.

Sorry, sir! Sorry, I'm sure! . . . I swear by Almighty God that what I shall say in evidence in this Court shall be the truth, the whole truth and nothing but the truth.

You were, I believe, butler and parlourman to Mr Maxwell Brunton, deceased?

Yes, sir.

And how long, Jennings, have you been in service at 44 Rajah Gardens?

Two years, sir, and six months.

At what time, Jennings, did you see your master for the last time alive?

Can't swear exactly to the minute, sir, but somewhere around 9 p.m.

Where was this?

At dinner, sir. After I brought in the port for the master and the other two gentlemen he said, as he always said: 'There's nothing more, Jennings!' and I says: 'Thank you, sir.' And that was the last time I ever saw 'im alive, sir.

Now, Jennings, you have heard the evidence of the previous witnesses, particularly that of Mr Harrison?

Yes, sir.

Do you agree with Mr Harrison's statement as regards the sequence of events, so far as you know them?

Yes, sir.

Will you please tell the Court, then, as briefly as you can, what happened after Mr Harrison waked you up at approximately half-past two.

Mr 'Arrison, sir, 'e come up and shook me awake like—well, really it was the missus what woke me, 'cause she woke first, an' she sez: 'Jennings! 'Ere's Mr 'Arrison and oh, Gawd, wot's 'appened?' an' I gets up and I sees it's Mr 'Arrison and Mr 'Arrison 'e sez to me 'e sez: 'Your master's been killed,' and I sez, 'Wot?' and he sez, 'Your master's been killed,' and I sez, 'Oh, my Gawd!' . . .

An' then Mr 'Arrison 'e sez for me to go and fetch a roz—policeman, sir, because 'e thinks there's been foul play. So I quiets the missus down, slips on my dressing-gown and runs out and finds the sergeant what give evidence just now, sir, at the corner of the Square and brings 'im in. After that, sir, it's just the same as what the sergeant 'imself and Mr 'Arrison 'ave told you. What I mean is, sir, that so far as I knows, it's the same. That's to say, sir, what I mean: when they give evidence about what I knows 'appened, me bein' there, they was right. About the other, what 'appened when I wasn't there, o' course I can't say like.

I see. So you corroborate the previous evidence so far as the incidents related had come into your knowledge?

That's right, sir. That's what I said.

Now, Jennings, I'm going to put a few questions to you, and I would like to make it clear to you first that it is your duty to give truthful answers to these questions—being as brief as you can—and not to allow any outside consideration whatsoever to influence you in those answers. Do you follow me?

Puffectly, sir.

Very well, then. I want to ask you first, Jennings, whether it came to your knowledge in any way that Mr Maxwell Brunton had quarrelled, on the day preceding the morning of his death, with any other member of the family?

No, sir.

You're sure, Jennings?

. . . Yes, sir.

You hesitated. Why?

Did I 'esitate, sir? I'm sure I never noticed meself.

So you were not aware at all that there had been any, shall we say, disagreements between your master and any other member of the household?

No, sir. Leastways, not if you don't count Syd—Mr 'Arrison, sir.

Oh! So there was a disagreement, was there, between Mr Brunton and Mr Harrison?

Couldn't say whether it was what you'd call a disagreement exactly like, sir, but I must say as I did notice that the master 'ad slipped Mr 'Arrison a ras—'ad told Mr 'Arrison off a bit, sir.

How was this, Jennings?

Well, it was like this. Miss Claire—that's Mrs Bayford, sir; I'm afraid we all call 'er Miss Claire, I suppose it's along of the mistress not seeming to be able to remember that Miss Claire's married—Miss Claire, she sez to me in the afternoon when I went into the libery to see if the cigarette boxes was all right, did I know whether the master was in and was he up in the study? I said yes, the master was up in the study, and she said, 'Thank you, Jennings, I think I'll go up and see him.' And with that, sir, she went out of the room.

What time was this, Jennings?

Now, let me see, sir. It wouldn't be so late as five, and it wouldn't be so early as four. I should say, sir, it would be about 'arf-past four. Anyways, about twenty minutes after this, sir, I was passing through the 'all and I sees Mr Adrian, and he calls out to me, 'Jennings, slip up and get me my cigar case from my room, will you? I'll be in the libery.' So I slips up, sir, and walks along to Mr Adrian's room and gets 'is case. As I'm coming out, sir, I sees Mr 'Arrison enterin' the study. As 'e opens the door I 'ears Miss Claire's voice, sir. Then as I'm walking along the passage I 'ears a sort of roar from the master. A bit startled like, I turns round and I sees Mr 'Arrison coming out of that room a lot quicker than 'e went in. I didn't take no notice, sir, it not bein' my place, an' I walks downstairs, sir, I dessay grinnin' a bit to meself. I gives Mr Adrian his cigar case and goes about the 'ouse on my work. I suppose that, sir, if you want the time, would be about quarter to five. Anyways, I didn't go upstairs again until about a quarter after five, and then it's to go and ask the master, as it was part of my duty to do, whether he'd like anythink in the way of refreshment brought up to the study, as 'e 'adn't been down to tea in the drawin'-room. Just as I gets to the landing, Mr 'Arrison comes by me and walks along to the study. I follows 'im. Before 'e gets to the study door it opens and out comes Miss Claire. Mr 'Arrison, 'e stops and says something to 'er, but she doesn't seem to take no notice but comes right straight on. Mr 'Arrison, 'e goes on too, the other way, into the study. I passes Miss Claire, sir. The study door's shut and I 'ears the master goin' for Mr 'Arrison proper. I'd 'alf expected it was because of Miss Claire. What I mean, sir, I guessed the master was in a bad temper. Well, sir, I goes into the study—

One moment, Jennings. What was it about Mrs Bayford that made you suspect that your master was in a mood in which he was likely to reprimand Mr Harrison?

Beg pardon, sir?

I think you heard what I said, Jennings. What was it about Mrs Bayford that made you suspect that your master was in a mood in which he was likely to reprimand Mr Harrison?

I dunno, sir. All I know is that when I got to the study the master—

Come, come, Jennings! This won't do! You suggested—I don't

*know whether you intended to, but suggest it you did—that there
was something in Mrs Bayford's demeanour as she left the study
which indicated to you that Mr Maxwell Brunton might be out
of temper.*

I'm sure, sir, I dunno 'ow I managed to give you that idear.
I—

*Jennings! This very palpable fencing won't do you any good
at all. What was it about Mrs Bayford's demeanour that led you
to expect Mr Brunton to be out of temper?*

Well, sir . . . Well, sir . . . If you must 'ave it, sir, Miss Claire—
she was, well, I think she 'ad been—cryin' a bit, sir. I can't see
what that's got to do with it, sir. Dunno whatever made me call
to mind or mention such a thing.

*Never mind that, Jennings. So Mrs Bayford was crying, and
Mr Harrison went into the study, and as soon as he entered it
Mr Brunton began to upbraid him?*

Up-what 'im, sir?

Mr Brunton began to reprimand him?

Yes, sir. The master, well, sir, 'e was tellin' Mr 'Arrison off
proper.

About what, Jennings?

No idear at all, sir. All I 'eard was the general sort of note,
as you might say, of the tick-off. As I got to the door Mr 'Arrison
come out again, for the second time that afternoon. Beggin'
your pardon, sir, I must say that I smiled. That was the second
time that day I'd seen Mr 'Arrison in trouble.

*Never mind, Jennings. When you went in, how did you find
Mr Brunton's manner as far as you were concerned?*

Just the same as usual, sir, when 'e was in one of his other
moods. He 'ad three moods, as you might say, sir. Short, friendly,
and what I and Mrs Jennings used to call 'the Juke.'

*All right, Jennings. I take it that you mean to inform the
Court that although Mr Brunton's manner may have been curt
he was not, so far as you could see, unusually angry or upset?*

That's right, sir.

Now, Jennings. Having been in Mr Brunton's service for this considerable time, you must have known something of his habits. I want you to tell the Court—remembering what I said just now of the necessity for speaking the truth as best you know it— whether, to your knowledge, Mr Brunton was—er—was—shall we say, excessively fond of the other sex.

. . . .

Come, now, Jennings. Don't keep the Court waiting. You heard my question.

Well, sir, it's very 'ard for me to say like. Mr Brunton, he was a gentleman, as you might say, fond of doing himself very well like. If you take my meaning, sir, he liked to do himself very well. What I mean to say, sir, is 'e was a very open-'anded, open-'earted sort of gentleman, and 'im being such a fine looking man as you might say, well, there's no denying that 'e didn't exactly 'ate women. Not of course, sir, that I've 'eard of any 'arm, but there it is. Mr Brunton—

Jennings, you know you are not answering questions at all. This rambling on is merely wasting the time of the Court. Did you or did you not know whether Mr Maxwell Brunton was in the habit of forming intimate relations with women other than his wife?

'Ow could *I* say, sir? Naturally the servants all gets to know this-and-that about the master of the family, but if it's a good servants' 'all they don't get to know too much . . .

Jennings, I have here a copy of the statement which you made to Inspector Syme on Thursday last together with copies of your replies to his questions. I am afraid I cannot reconcile the answer you have just given us with one of those replies.

'Scuse me, sir, but I suppose you're referring to that business about the parlourmaid Ellen. I must say, sir, the way things get put into a man's mouth by the police and then get twisted all round, well . . . What I mean to say, sir, is certainly the girl *did* leave, and certainly she shot off 'er mouth a lot about the master, but me and Mrs Jennings, at any rate, didn't believe not a quarter of what she said. Very pretty little bit she was, sir, but incapable of speakin' the truth.

I see. So this girl—let me see . . . Ellen Richards—this girl left the employ of Mr Brunton very suddenly?

Yes, sir.

And she went, apparently, without giving notice, on the twenty-third of February last, having been in the house only a week?

That's right, sir.

She gave as her reason for leaving the conduct of Mr Brunton?

Couldn't say what reason she give, sir, but certainly she shot off 'er mouth a lot in the kitchen, and then she rushes upstairs and packs 'er things in 'er box and dashes out of the 'ouse before you could say Jack Robinson. It's my belief, sir, it was something else altogether. Nothing to do with the master.

Your beliefs are nothing to do with the Court at the moment. When we wish for them we will ask you for them. I should perhaps tell you that the girl Richards has been interviewed by the police . . .

We will leave her now, and go on to ask you this question—and please, Jennings, remember that your statement may be subject to a check in these papers that I have here. You must understand that personal considerations such as the good name of the family in which you are in service cannot and must not enter into this inquiry. You are here to tell the truth.

Yes, sir. Very good, sir.

Very well. Please tell us whether during your years of service in the household any other similar cases occurred.

Not so far as I know, sir.

Do you remember, Jennings, a lady secretary whom Mr Brunton employed from the January before last until last July?

Miss Mayne, sir. Yes, sir.

That is correct. Miss Gladys Mayne. Now! Miss Mayne left rather abruptly, didn't she?

Don't know, sir. She left certainly. Whether it was abruptly like, 'ow could I say?

I think you could, Jennings. I must warn you that, however much you are to be sympathised with in a difficult position, I don't like the way you are giving your answers. Now! Did you ever hear the reason for Miss Mayne's leaving the house?

No, sir.

You are sure?

Yes, sir.

What was your own opinion for the reason of her sudden departure?

Didn't 'ave none, sir.

Did Miss Mayne appear to be happy and contented during all the time she was in the house?

Absolutely, sir. As 'appy as the day is long, as you might say. Never saw a 'appier young lady in my life. Seemed very 'appy about 'er work and 'appier in the 'ouse. Very 'appy young lady, sir!

So that you think her work for Mr Brunton and Mr Brunton's behaviour toward herself gave her no cause for unhappiness?

I don't think, sir. I *know.*

I see . . . Can you explain, Jennings, how it was that when Miss Mayne left so hurriedly she was in a state of great distress— tears and so forth—and had been in such a state for the past forty-eight hours?

.   .   .   .   .   .

Come, Jennings! Please answer.

'Fraid I can't sir. I don't remember. If you say she was un'appy about going away, you must be right, 'aving got it from the police or Mr 'Arrison. But I recolleck nothing at all.

Do you wish that answer to go on record, Jennings?

Yes, sir.

You are not aware, then, Jennings, of a scene which took place in the household thirty-six hours prior to Miss Mayne's departure?

Scene, sir? No, sir.

You were not, in fact, aware that on the Wednesday night before Miss Mayne's departure on the Friday, Mrs Brunton had entered Mr Brunton's study at about half an hour after midnight and found Mr Brunton and Miss Mayne together in such circumstances that she demanded Miss Mayne's immediate withdrawal from the house?

Me, sir? Certainly not, sir.

You were not, on that night, wakened by the bell in your room! You did not go downstairs to find Mrs Brunton waiting for you outside her room? Mrs Brunton did not tell you that you were to go out and fetch a taxi at once because Miss Mayne was leaving the house? You did not, in fact, go down to the hall on the way to telephone or leave the house in search of a taxi? You were not stopped in the hall by your master who told you to return immediately to bed and take no notice of Mrs Brunton's orders?

.   .   .   .   .   .

Come, Jennings! Did these events take place or not?

Well, sir. What can I—Yes, sir.

How do you reconcile that answer, Jennings, with the one you gave to my last question?

I—I—well, sir—oh, yes, sir, I remember. It was just as you said, but Mrs Brunton never mentioned no name. She never said 'oo the taxi was for.

I see. You note the witness's answer, gentlemen . . .

Now, Jennings! It seems hopeless to try to get any real evidence from you. I am going to ask you a few more general questions and then tell you to stand down; but I must warn you that you will very likely be wanted again, and if and when you are, it will be very much wiser for you to give direct answers to anything you are asked. The first of the remaining questions I have to put to you this time, is: Are you aware of any reason why any person who was an inmate of 44 Rajah Gardens on the night of Thursday last should have any reason for wishing the death of Mr Maxwell Brunton?

No, sir.

Have you any reason for supposing that the various quarrels and misunderstandings which took place between Mr Brunton and members of the household that day and which have been described to us by you and other witnesses, were anything more than misunderstandings? Were, in fact, deadly and serious quarrels?

No, sir.

So far as you know, life upon that Thursday and the days immediately preceding it was entirely normal in the household?

Yes, sir.

Very well, Jennings, you may stand down. Remember that you may be wanted again . . . I am assuming, gentlemen, that you have no more questions to ask this witness at this stage?

Call Enid Brunton!

VI

Enid Kathleen Brunton

What is your full name?

Enid Kathleen Brunton.

Will you please take the oath.

I swear by Almighty God that what I shall say in evidence in this Court shall be the truth, the whole truth and nothing but the truth.

You are the widow of the deceased?

Yes.

Having concluded these formalities, Mrs Brunton, I have to proceed to ask you a few questions. I need not say that it will be to your advantage and to ours if you will answer these as concisely as possible . . . You have heard the evidence of all the preceding witnesses?

Yes.

In particular, the evidence of Mr Sydney Harrison, your husband's secretary?

Yes.

You did not see your husband alive after that time when he came into the drawing-room at eleven o'clock and talked for a while and then left again for his study?

No.

At what time did you retire?

At eleven-thirty, at the same time as the rest of the party except my daughter—Mrs Bayford—and Mr Hargreaves.

And you went straight to your room?

Yes.

And you did not leave your room between that time and the time when you were roused by the news of your husband's death?

No.

And you heard no unusual sounds during that time?

No.

Are there any facts in any of the evidence hitherto given with which you disagree?

No.

You will remember that in his evidence Mr Harrison stated that he inadvertently became aware that you and your husband had been apparently quarrelling? That, of course, was when you entered the study and desired to speak to Mr Brunton. Mr Harrison accordingly left it, and having been told by Mr Brunton to return in ten minutes, he returned before your interview with your husband had ended. You remember this?

Yes.

Had you, in fact, been having any disagreement with your husband?

Yes.

Was it a serious disagreement? Amounting to a quarrel?

That is difficult to answer. There are degrees in these things.

Quite. But what I am trying to get at, Mrs Brunton, is how bitter the disagreement or quarrel was. Was it a greater disagreement than you had ever had with Mr Brunton previously?

No.

But all the same for that, a fairly serious matter?

Yes.

Will you please tell the Court what it was about?

Can I be forced to answer that question?

No. Not in this Court. Nor can you be forced in any other court. But I would like to impress upon you, Mrs Brunton, that this is an inquiry into the manner in which your husband met his death. You have heard the police surgeon's statement to the effect that the injury which caused that death could not have been self-inflicted or accidental. And, therefore, you must realise that the injury was in all probability inflicted by some other person. This means that we are investigating a matter of the very gravest nature, and that, therefore, no stone can be left unturned. Anyone withholding information or refusing to answer questions which the Court deems necessary must obviously place themselves, by deliberately hindering the proceedings, in a very grave situation. I hope you understand me?

Perfectly. Do you still wish me to tell you the cause of my quarrel with my husband on the day of his death?

Please.

It was about a woman. I had learnt, on reliable information, that my husband had been enjoying a liaison with this woman. I told him that I knew. I reminded him of promises he had made before. I asked him to put an end to his intimacy with this woman. He was very angry. Angrier, I think, than I had ever seen him before. He accused me of having had him spied upon, and I admitted the accusation. He threatened—he threatened—

.   .   .   .   .   .

Shall I ask the clerk to get you a glass of water, Mrs Brunton?

No, thank you, I am sorry. I won't do that again. Shall I go on?

Please.

My husband threatened to leave me. He had never done such a thing before in all our life together. He also made other vague threats. He was, as I said just now, angrier than I had ever seen him.

May we have the name of this woman, Mrs Brunton? I take it that you know it?

I do. But is it necessary for me to give it in Court? She has no connection whatsoever with this . . . She doesn't even live in London. My husband's time with her was spent away from London. She has never been in or near our house.

I see. I don't think, Mrs Brunton, that it will be necessary for us to insist upon a public announcement of this name at this stage, but perhaps you would write it down and hand it in to me.

.   .   .   .   .   .

Thank you . . . Now, Mrs Brunton: some rather painful questions, I am afraid, but both you and I have our duty to do . . . You were married to Mr Brunton, I think you said, twenty-seven years ago?

Yes. I was eighteen when we married. He was nine years older than I.

And during that time, as I understand from the general trend of the evidence, and your evidence in particular, there have been several instances of temporary infidelity on Mr Brunton's side?

Yes.

You knew of all these?

I cannot say. I knew of many.

Did you ever consider obtaining a divorce from Mr Brunton?

Never.

But you had other quarrels with him on the subject of these infidelities?

Many.

Apart from this distressing side of his character, was Mr Brunton a good husband to you?

Very, very good.

And a good father to his children?

To my daughter, yes. To my son, sometimes.

It may seem rather a strange question, Mrs Brunton, but this is a strange affair: What were your feelings towards Mr Brunton? I do not mean at any one stage of your life, but taken over the whole of your married life?

I loved him.

In spite of his infidelities and the fact that you considered he was not always a good father to your son?

In spite of these things.

Mrs Brunton, you say that you knew that Mr Brunton's liaison with this woman—whose name you have written down for me—took place in all its phases outside London.

Yes.

You could, if necessary, prove that?

Yes.

Can you tell us, Mrs Brunton, from your knowledge of your husband, whether this liaison would preclude the possibility of other and temporary intrigues?

I can tell you. It would have been quite possible for my husband to have been associated with another woman as well over the same period.

Possibly in London?

Possibly in London.

Possibly, Mrs Brunton, inside your house?

Oh God! . . . I am sorry. That is possible, sir. But I do not think that it was so.

I am sorry, Mrs Brunton, but I have to finish this line of questioning.

Please go on.

Very well, then. You say that it is not likely, during the time immediately preceding his death, that your husband was conducting an intrigue with anyone living in or frequently visiting your house. And you say that you do not think this situation existed. Does that 'think,' Mrs Brunton, actually mean that you cannot be sure?

It . . . Yes.

Thank you. Will you please tell me now whether there have, of late, been many women visitors to your house with whom it is possible or likely that Mr Brunton had been carrying on an intrigue.

When exactly do you mean by 'of late'?

Let us say within the last six weeks or—two months. That is from a time approximately two months ago up to the day of your husband's death.

There have not. There have been no visitors.

Except, of course, Miss Lamort? So, Mrs Brunton, if there had been another liaison, of which you knew nothing, in addition to the one of which you know, going on before your husband's death it was either one which was conducted, like the one of which

*you did know, outside the house, or one which was conducted
with somebody within the house?*

That is so.

*I understand from your previous evidence, Mrs Brunton, that
you had been having some sort of watch kept upon Mr Brunton's
movements outside the house. Am I correct?*

Quite correct . . . I *had—*

You were saying, Mrs Brunton?

Nothing. I said that I agreed that I had been having my
husband watched.

*May we take it, then, that if this other possible liaison of which
I have been speaking had taken place* outside *the house, you
would have known about it?*

You may.

Without doubt?

Without doubt.

*Therefore, Mrs Brunton, if this possible intrigue were, in fact,
going on up to the time of your husband's death, it was both
within your house and with someone at that time, at least, living
within your house?*

If you must go on with that assumption: Yes.

*Please forgive me, Mrs Brunton. I am afraid I must carry on
in my own way . . . Now: assuming this intrigue was in your
own house, can you tell us—I am sorry for this, Mrs Brunton,
but I must conduct the inquiry as I think best—can you tell us
who, being resident in your house at the time of your husband's
death and for some little time at least previous to that, would be
the most likely partner in such a possible liaison?*

.   .   .   .

Was my question clear, Mrs Brunton?

Quite clear. I am afraid that I cannot answer it.

You can make no conjecture?

I am afraid I cannot answer your question.

*Very well, Mrs Brunton. Just two more questions and then
I think I shall be able to conclude your evidence at least for*

*the present. In the first place, you have heard the suggestion
contained in the evidence of a previous witness to the effect
that your husband and son also quarrelled on the day of his
death?*

Yes.

Have you any knowledge of this quarrel or disagreement?

Yes.

Will you please tell us what you know, then.

Early that morning my son came to me and told me that he
had got something to ask his father which he did not think
would meet with approval. He was very nervous about it all. I
tried to calm him and suggested that perhaps he would like me
to speak to his father instead, but he wouldn't have that. From
a small boy Adrian has always been very courageous. All the
more so because he is very nervous naturally. But he just *makes*
himself do things. I think perhaps the scene with his father was
more violent than it need have been just because Adrian was
so nervous and apprehensive before it began.

*Can you give the jury, Mrs Brunton, any idea of what this
quarrel was about?*

Generally speaking, yes. For the details, you will have to ask
my son himself when he is before you. All I know is that it was
about a young woman with whom he is very deeply in love. He
wanted his father's consent to his engagement and was afraid
that he would not get it.

*I suppose we are to gather, Mrs Brunton, that consent was
withheld?*

Yes. I am afraid Adrian had chosen a bad day to approach
his father. I tried to persuade him to put it off.

*May I ask, Mrs Brunton, whether you yourself approved of
your son's choice?*

I am afraid I have not yet met the lady, but I am sure that
my son would not have such deep and sincere feelings for
anyone unsatisfactory.

I see. As you say, Mrs Brunton, I have no doubt that we shall get more definite information from your son. Before we leave the matter entirely, however, I should like to ask you whether you saw your son immediately after the interview.

No, I did not. It must have been at least two hours later that I saw him.

What was his state of mind then, Mrs Brunton—so far as you could judge?

He was naturally most upset. I tried to soothe him. I told him also that the best thing he could do was to let the matter rest for a day or two, when both he and I would speak to his father again.

Did that seem to satisfy him at all?

Yes.

So that after seeing you and getting your counsel his ill-feeling toward his father appeared in some measure to evaporate?

I cannot say. We changed the subject.

What was your son's attitude toward his father when they met, at dinner and later that day? And if it comes to that, Mr Brunton's attitude toward his son?

My husband appeared to be conciliatory. He hated hurting people's feelings. He often did so, but he was always genuinely sorry afterward.

And Mr Adrian Brunton?

My son is much younger. I am afraid that, quite naturally, he did not respond much to his father's advances. Really, sir, that is quite natural, if you come to think of it.

I see. Now, Mrs Brunton, you have heard the previous evidence. In this evidence there was contained, besides the suggestion that your son and your husband disagreed that day, another to the effect that your daughter and your husband disagreed that day. Do you know anything of this?

Nothing at all.

Neither your husband nor Mrs Bayford made any mention to you of any misunderstanding or disagreement?

None whatever.

And since your husband's death, Mrs Bayford has made no mention of this to you?

None whatsoever.

Thank you. One last question. Apart from these family troubles and the other matters of which we have spoken, do you know whether your husband had, prior to his death, been worrying about any other outside matters?

Not to my knowledge.

He had seemed, in fact, to be his normal self?

Entirely.

Over a period of, let us say, a month or longer before his death?

Yes.

Thank you, Mrs Brunton. I have no more questions to put to you at this stage, and I do not imagine the jury will have . . . Is that so, gentlemen? . . . Thank you . . . Mrs Brunton, if you will stand down.

Call Adrian Brunton.

VII

Adrian Brunton

What is your full name?

Adrian Brunton.

Will you please take the oath?

Do I have to take the oath?

No, Mr Brunton, this Court has no power to force you to give your evidence under oath, but I can only suggest that to do so is both advisable and helpful.

Why?

I beg your pardon?

I said why.

Mr Brunton, I am afraid this is a court of inquiry, not a debating club! Am I to understand that you refuse to take the oath and will give your evidence without having done so?

No.

I am afraid I cannot understand your conduct, Mr Brunton!

Quite easy to follow! You said would I please take the oath. I said: Must I? You said: No. However, I'll go through the gabble.

Will you please hand Mr Brunton the book?

I swear by Almighty God that what I shall say in evidence in this Court shall be the truth, the whole truth and nothing but the truth.

You are the only son of Maxwell Brunton, deceased?

Whoever told you that?

Mr Brunton, I must ask you to treat this Court with the respect due to it.

Didn't know I wasn't!

Silence in the Court! I will have silence! Now then: When, Mr Brunton, did you last see your father?

Just when the others did. He came down to the drawing-room while we were playing bridge.

And you agree with the time, Mr Brunton, as given by the other witnesses?

Yes.

You did not see him again alive after that?

I said that was the last time I saw him, and I meant it.

Your room, Mr Brunton, is next door to your father's study, isn't it?

Yes. That's to say, mine's the last room at the back of the original building of the house. The study was built on. Can't hear what's going on, or anything of that sort, if that's what you're after.

What I am 'after', Mr Brunton, will appear in the course of my questions. No such remarks are needed from the witnesses.

Couldn't we get on with it?

What time was it when you retired to your room, Mr Brunton?

Good God! It seems to me we keep going round and round the same old circle. All the other people have told you we all went up except Hargreaves and Claire, my sister, at half-past eleven.

And you didn't leave your room after retiring to it at half-past eleven?

Yes, I did.

When and what for?

About ten minutes after I got there. Lavatory.

You returned straight to your room?

Obviously.

And went, I suppose, straight to bed?

Do you think I'm a damn fool? You know perfectly well that that little swine Harrison told you that after he came—after he had found the Guv'nor, that I wasn't undressed. No; I didn't go to bed. I didn't feel like sleep. I'd only gone up because I wanted to be alone. I took off my dinner jacket and put on a dressing-gown.

And you sat up alone like that in your room for three hours?

Pretty simple, isn't it? I came up at half-past eleven. Harrison came in at a quarter-past two. Three hours less a quarter.

May I ask, Mr Brunton, what you were doing during this time?

No harm in asking. I was thinking.

May we ask what those thoughts were that occupied you for such a long period of time?

Ask away. You know already. You know from my mother's evidence.

Do you mean to tell us, Mr Brunton, that you were thinking about the disagreement you had had with your father that afternoon, and the situation which had led up to that disagreement?

Yes. Quite natural, isn't it? Fellow wants to get married. Can't afford to do it on his own. Asks his father. Nothing doing. Fellow isn't feeling much like sleep.

During those three hours, Mr Brunton, did you hear anything unusual going on in the house?

Don't remember hearing a sound. You don't hear much in my room, anyhow.

Will you please tell us, Mr Brunton, the exact situation at the end of your quarrel with your father. Perhaps it would be better if you would tell us the whole thing. We understand, from previous evidence, that the interview ended, at any rate, in high words.

Plenty of words and some of them high! Very easy to explain. Asked father whether he'd increase my allowance to what I considered enough to get married on. He said, 'No.' I said, 'Why?' He had the damn— My fiancée didn't meet with his approval.

May I ask, Mr Brunton, on what grounds he based his disapproval?

You can ask until you're black in the face. You'll get no answer from me. I think you're inquiring into how my father came to get killed, not into the histories of people who've nothing to do with that.

Very well. We will leave that matter. At least for the moment. I would like to take this opportunity of saying, though, that I should be glad if you would moderate both your manner and your language.

You moderate your questions and I'll try.

How, Mr Brunton, was the matter left between your father and yourself? What, I mean, was the situation at the end of the interview?

Just like that. I asked. He refused.

There was nothing, then, to suggest that the matter could be reopened between you? Your father, I take it, was final, or seemed so?

Dead final. I knew him pretty well. I didn't tell mother when I was talking to her afterwards, but I'm perfectly sure that he would never have altered his mind. It was being so sure that put me in such a state.

You do not agree, then, with Mrs Brunton, that you had merely approached your father at an unpropitious time?

No. He'd have been the same at any time. That's what I think, anyhow.

So you do not agree with the implications of your mother and other witnesses in their evidence that Mr Brunton was, shall we say, in ill-temper during the day preceding his death?

Didn't say so, did I? Certainly he was. Damn bad mood. But that was nothing with father. I'm going by what I know of him generally.

Have you any idea, Mr Brunton, reverting to one part of your answer, as to what could have put your father in this 'bad mood'? Any idea, I mean, apart from these matters of which we have already heard, such as the disagreement with Mrs Brunton?

Yes.

.　　　.　　　.　　　.　　　.　　　.

Well! We are waiting, Mr Brunton.

What for?

Please do not quibble. We are waiting for you to tell us, as I think you know perfectly well, what your idea is of the cause of your father's ill-temper.

Hargreaves.

Please be more explicit, Mr Brunton. Conciseness is to be desired, I admit, but not conciseness which leaves a witness's meaning in the air.

Good God! You asked me what I thought put the Guv'nor—my father, in that mood, and I told you Hargreaves. I meant it. If I did know why, I'd tell you, but I don't. All I know is that when I saw him first that Thursday and the day before, he said a couple of things—just remarks here and there—which showed me that he didn't like having Hargreaves in the house.

Can you remember the words of these remarks, Mr Brunton?

No.

Not even a slightly more detailed gist?

No.

When were these remarks made?

The one on Thursday was made when I first went into the study. When I was breaking the ice. Didn't take much notice of it. Too much occupied with my own troubles.

All you can tell us, then, is that you gathered that the person and presence of Mr Hargreaves was distasteful to your father?

I didn't say anything about person. You're right about presence, though. What I mean is that I got a general feeling that it was not so much that he didn't like Hargreaves, but he didn't like Hargreaves being about the place.

Did your father, Mr Brunton, know Mr Hargreaves well?

Hardly at all. Hargreaves was a friend of Claire's, my sister, years ago, before she was married, but we didn't see much of him. Knew him, of course, and all that. But not well. About the time Claire got married he went abroad. He'd only just come back when he came to stay. My sister asked my mother to ask him. Old friends and all that.

You can give us nothing more definite, then, Mr Brunton? I am sorry to keep worrying, but this is all rather important. You can give us nothing more definite about the apparent dislike for Mr Hargreaves on your father's part?

No. Said so once.

Perhaps you can tell us then whether this dislike of Mr Hargreaves's presence was shared by any other member of the family. Yourself, for instance? Or your mother?

Can't speak for my mother. She certainly never *showed* anything.

And yourself, Mr Brunton?

Nothing against Hargreaves myself. Don't see much of him. Don't think much about him. Too much occupied with my own trouble.

And your sister, of course?

My sister will be giving evidence, I suppose, on her own account.

How long has Mr Hargreaves been staying in the house, Mr Brunton?

Why the devil do you keep asking me questions when you know the answers? But I suppose you must. Can't say definitely. Just over a week, I think.

I see that I must remind you again, Mr Brunton, that your manner is not one to be desired. Please keep your criticisms of this Court and the way it is being conducted to yourself. Confine yourself to answering my questions and answering them in a proper manner.

After all this I can't remember whether there is one for me to answer or not.

I will supply it. You have heard all the previous evidence, Mr Brunton?

I haven't been asleep.

You will remember, then, that during your mother's evidence I put to her a series of questions which elicited the fact that if an intrigue of your father's had been going on unknown to her during the time immediately prior to his death, such an intrigue must have been with someone resident in the house.

Yes. I remember the foul business.

Mr Brunton! *I really must insist that you mend your behaviour in this Court.*

Sorry. Sorry.

At the end of that series of questions I put a question—I can assure you that I did not like putting it—to which your mother stated that she could not reply.

You mean the one about if my father had had a spare mistress in the house, who would it have been?

If you care to put it in that manner, Mr Brunton, yes.

What the hell does it matter what manner I put it in? Means the same thing, doesn't it? Well, I'll answer it. There've been so many bagfuls of stinking linen washed in this room already that one more won't hurt. *If* there was—mind that '*if*,' Mr Coroner—if there was, what you call an 'intrigue' going on in the house, I should give it as my opinion that it was with my mother's maid.

You mean Jeannette Bokay?

Obviously Bocquet. My mother's only got one maid.

Do you mean to suggest to the Court, Mr Brunton, that you have reason for supposing that this Jeannette Bokay was carrying on an intrigue with your father?

I asked you to mind that '*if*,' didn't I? I don't *know* anything. I don't *think* anything. You said if there *was* one, who would it be with? I say, if there *was* one, the answer is Bocquet.

Why, Mr Brunton?

Eh?

I said, 'Why?' What are the facts behind this reasoning on your part?

You will probably understand when you have Bocquet up here! Oh, damn it! Let's cut a long story short. My father couldn't keep away from women. *You* know that by this time, and every damn halfpenny paper will have it on every front page this evening. What's it matter what *I* say? You want to know why I choose Bocquet for this imaginary mistress you're trying to create. I'll tell you. The answer's quite obvious. Because—she's—good—to—look—at. My father may have been a womaniser, but he did have taste.

No doubt, Mr Brunton. Bokay, however, is not the only attractive woman, apart from his own family, under your father's roof.

Eh! . . . Good *God!* You know you oughtn't to be *allowed* to run this job! You're a foul-minded . . . Do they *let* you do this sort of thing?

Mr Brunton, you must please control yourself, or I shall have to take other methods to ensure that you do. To some extent I can sympathise with your feelings and consequent manner and indignation. But not beyond a point. You used the word 'foul' just now. Let me remind you. Mr Brunton, that a murder may be a foul business. Will you please give me your undertaking to mend your behaviour?

.   .   .   .   .   .

Mr Brunton!

Oh, all right. I'll be good.

Very well. I take it from your reception of my last remarks in regard to the question I had asked you, that you still adhere to your view that if there was an intrigue going on between your father and a member of the household at the time of his death, the other party to the intrigue must have been Jeannette Bokay?

Yes.

Have you any other reasons besides the one you gave just now for making this statement? Now, please . . .

Yes.

Will you please give them to the Court?

My father had had a line on Bocquet before.

Indeed? When was this?

About eighteen months ago.

You are certain?

Yes.

How?

I came in very late one night—being very quiet, not to wake

the house. Didn't put light on downstairs. Just as I opened the door of my room, the study door opened and Bocquet came out. She was in pyjamas.

And your father was in the study?

Obviously. I heard him.

And the time was?

Very late, as I said. Near as I can remember, about half-past two, quarter to three.

Do you know, Mr Brunton, whether either your father or Bokay was aware that you had seen her leaving the study?

They weren't. I hadn't switched on my light. As a matter of fact, I'd just half closed my door behind me when I heard the study door open and happened to look out through the crack of my door.

And you made no reference of what you saw to anyone?

Why should I?

You did not tell your mother?

Why should I? She'd had enough of that sort of trouble. Even if I'd told her and she'd got rid of the girl, it'd only've been the same thing with someone else. I wouldn't have mentioned it now if it hadn't been for the suggestion *you* made.

I see. And so you were satisfied to let this intrigue, which you knew about, go on without saying anything to anybody?

Surely that's my business? As a matter of fact, I did speak to my father. We had a row about it.

There is one thing I don't quite follow, Mr Brunton. That is, you were very particular just now with your conditional clause. You stated that you knew nothing and thought nothing about the possibility of Bokay's being your father's mistress during the time immediately prior to his death and yet, here you are telling us that she was, *in fact, his mistress.*

Half a minute! Half a minute! That was eighteen months ago. The whole thing lasted—I don't know how long it had been going on, of course—but the whole thing lasted, after that time when I saw her, coming out of the study, not more than a month. They never did last very long.

I take it, Mr Brunton, that you are trying to tell the Court that this liaison was terminated?

That's right.

You know this?

Sure of it. My father told me himself.

But would that—

Half a minute. My father never told lies. I mean in that sort of way. If you taxed him with a thing he gave you the truth. He must, of course, have lied and acted lies about women while he was having affairs with them, but *they'd* be just what you'd call convenience lies. As I say, if you taxed him with a thing, you got the truth. And he came and told me that the Bocquet thing was over. He was a bit worried about it. I think he'd expected the girl to give up her job and go when he'd finished with her. He said as much. He'd have made it all right as far as money went. But she wasn't having any. That's what he told me. Of course, he couldn't very well ask mother to get rid of her.

You believed this?

Certainly. I've told you my father never lied. Also the way the girl behaved was proof. Even mother noticed something odd about her. She seemed to be in a sort of brooding rage for weeks. Then she got over it.

And you never saw a recrudescence of your father's—of this liaison?

Never. I merely said, in answer to your question, that *if* there was an affair going on in the house, it must've been a revival of the Bocquet one.

But, in fact, you do not know that this was so?

How many times have I got to tell you? No. I have no grounds for suspicion. Seems damn unlikely to me.

I see. One more question, Mr Brunton, and may I please remind you that such questions as these have to be asked? Now that your father is dead, I take it that you will be in a position to contract the marriage to which he would not consent.

You take it right.

I understand, Mr Brunton, that the bulk of your father's considerable fortune comes to you?

It does.

Were you aware of this before his death?

Look here, blast— Sorry. Yes.

Did you happen to know, Mr Brunton, before your father's death, of any of his intentions in regard to minor bequests?

Only generally. He told me at one time and another what he was doing for mother. Leaving her an annuity of £5000. And Claire an annuity of £3000, and one or two small things I can't remember. You can find them in that will. I can see a copy of it peeping out from under your papers.

And the residue of the estate which you have inherited, Mr Brunton, is, I understand, in the neighbourhood of £300,000?

Something like that. Have a look at your papers.

Well, Mr Brunton, I think that's all we have to ask you just at present. That is, unless any member of the jury has any question he would like to put . . . I see there are none. Thank you, Mr Brunton. You may stand down. We may want you again later.

I think that it is now time that we adjourned for luncheon. In view of the pressing nature of this inquiry I am going to ask you all to shorten the recess and be back here in forty-five minutes time, when I shall call the next witness—Claire Bayford.

VIII

CLAIRE BAYFORD

WHAT is your full name?

Claire Bayford.

Will you please take the oath?

I swear by Almighty God that what I shall say in evidence in this Court shall be the truth, the whole truth and nothing but the truth.

I understand that you are the only daughter of Maxwell Brunton, deceased?

Yes.

You have heard the evidence of the foregoing witnesses, Mrs Bayford?

Yes.

Is it correct that you were in the drawing-room with the rest of the family upon the fatal evening?

Yes.

And do you remember your father coming in for five minutes or so just after eleven o'clock?

Yes.

And that occasion was the last occasion upon which you saw him alive?

Yes.

I understand from previous evidence that you and Mr Hargreaves remained downstairs for longer than the rest of the household?

Yes.

At what time did you yourself, Mrs Bayford, go upstairs to your room?

I happen to know exactly. At ten minutes to twelve. I told

Mr Hargreaves I was very sleepy. We'd been out late dancing the night before. He looked at his watch and told me the time.

So that you were in your bedroom at five minutes to twelve at the latest? And Mr Hargreaves? Did he remain downstairs after you had left?

No. He came up with me. We said good-night at the head of the stairs and went into our rooms at the same time.

I see. And after you had got into your room, Mrs Bayford, did you leave it again that night?

No. Not until after—until after—

I quite understand. You did not leave your room, then, until you were roused after your father's death had been discovered?

No.

Did you go to bed?

Yes. When I first got upstairs. As I said, I was very tired. I undressed and got into bed at once. I thought I should go to sleep but somehow I couldn't. I tried reading, and that was no good; so at last I got up, slipped on some clothes, and sat down at my table to write my diary.

I see. And during these two and a half hours that you were in your room, did you hear any unusual sound at all from the rest of the house?

I don't remember hearing anything of any kind.

Thank you. Now, Mrs Bayford, you have heard the evidence of all the previous witnesses?

Yes.

You will have noticed, then, that mention has been made by more than one witness of your father's apparent dislike of Mr Hargreaves's presence in the house. Can you elucidate this for us in any way?

I—I think so. I—I—I suppose this is necessary?

Yes, Mrs Bayford. Please continue.

I think—I think—that Daddy—my father thought—didn't like Mr Hargreaves being there because he thought—he thought—that perhaps Mr Hargreaves and I might—might—just possibly get married.

I see. Was this attitude of your father's, do you know, Mrs Bayford, on account of Mr Hargreaves personally?

Oh, *no*! Daddy—my father liked Mr Hargreaves. No . . . If father was upset, it was because he thought that I should be going away again. He was awfully upset when I married and—and—

One moment, Mrs Bayford. I believe you were married for only a short time?

Yes. My husband died seven months after the wedding.

And you immediately came back to live with your family?

Yes.

I take it, Mrs Bayford, that you and your father were on very affectionate terms?

Yes. Very. He—he— Oh . . .!

.   .   .   .   .   .

Please hand this glass of water to Mrs Bayford.

I—I am so sorry.

Are you feeling well enough, Mrs Bayford, to continue?

Yes. I'm sorry. Please go on.

To pick up our thread, then, Mrs Bayford: You feel certain that this dislike which your father showed concerning Mr Hargreaves's presence in the house was due to his fear that you might become Mr Hargreaves's wife and so leave your family again?

That—that is so.

Are you, in fact, Mrs Bayford, engaged to Mr Hargreaves?

No.

I see—I see . . . But I assume that your father had good reason to suppose that—

Yes . . . You see—you see—Mr Hargreaves and I were very old friends. We've known each other since we were children. And—and—when Mr Hargreaves came back to England, I asked Daddy—my father, whether I could ask him to stay with us.

And he let me. And I think he could see. I am afraid I am not explaining myself very well.

Never mind, Mrs Bayford. I follow your meaning. I hope you realise that it is not pleasant for me personally to have to conduct this examination.

Oh! I do understand.

In previous evidence, Mrs Bayford—Jennings's, to be precise—it was stated that you came away from an interview you had with your father in his study on Thursday afternoon in such a manner that it would appear that you had been quarrelling with him.

Not quarrelling. No! D—my father and I never quarrelled. *Never!* I—I was unhappy. I was sort of mixed up. I—I can't explain.

Never mind, Mrs Bayford. We will take it—if I am wrong correct me—that you were suffering from mixed emotions at the thought of the possibility of leaving your father, conflicting, perhaps, with the desire that in certain circumstances you should leave him?

Thank you. That's quite right.

So that you had no quarrel or misunderstanding with your father?

Not on that day or *ever!*

Now, Mrs Bayford: I fear that the next part of my examination is going to be rather painful to you. It must, however, be gone through. I hope you understand the position.

I do. Perfectly.

You have heard the previous evidence. And you have heard the statement made by the various witnesses in regard—er—in regard to your father's relations with the other sex.

Yes.

Is this evidence and the trend of this evidence in accordance with your knowledge?

Yes.

Very well. I must now put to you the question which I have

*put to the last two witnesses, your mother and your brother. If
your father, at the time of his death, had been carrying on an
intrigue with someone living under his roof, whom do you
consider would be the most likely partner in this intrigue?*

I—I—Daddy—I—I can't answer! I'm sure it isn't a fair question. I *won't* answer! I don't care whether I'm supposed to
answer or not, but I *won't*! I couldn't anyhow, and I wouldn't
if I could. All this time, in this beastly place, all you vile people
have been doing nothing but harp, harp, harp, on Daddy and
women. Women! Women! Women! I *know* he was fond of
women. I *know* he couldn't keep away from women. I *know* it
was wrong of him, but that's all I've heard about him here. All!
Just that one thing. Always! All the time! I know it's a big thing
and a serious one. But it's bigger and more serious for some
people than it is for others. Who has told you anything about
what a wonderful man my father really was? Who has told you
about all the *good* things he did? Nobody! I can't, because if I
started to tell you I should never stop. Who has told you how
kind he was? How sympathetic! How understanding! Who has
told you about all the lame dogs he's put on their feet and never
told anybody? If you wanted to know anything about that you
had to peep and pry the way those people have been peeping
and prying about the one failing he *had* got. You've heard what
other people have had to put up with from him, but have you
heard what he had to put up with from other people? No! Have
you heard anything about other people's nerves? Other people's
tempers! Have you heard anything about when he was young
and hadn't got all his money, how other people spent what he
hadn't got and how he never complained? Never! Never! Never!
I am *sick* of hearing about him and women. He never hurt them,
so far as I know, and, anyway, they used to flock around him,
simply throwing themselves at him. Isn't it as much their fault
as his? Damn them!

Mrs Bayford! . . .

Oh! Stop talking! You've done all the talking here. I'm telling you something you haven't heard, and that is what you ought to know. You are the Coroner! You are supposed to be finding things out, and all the time you've only found out one thing about Daddy. Suppose he'd been a man who neglected his children! Suppose he'd been a man who never helped anyone! Suppose he'd been a man who, during the war, took a nice soft job in Whitehall! Suppose he'd been a man who was a secret drinker or drugger. Would all that have come out and been chewed about and clawed about and smelt round by all you people and his people? Of course it wouldn't! And yet all these things are sins! Surely, surely, surely, this business of sinning must vary with the sinner! . . . Oh! it makes me sick—sick, I tell you!

Mrs Bayford, please . . . We quite understand your natural—

Oh, *please* be quiet! . . . I am sorry . . . I won't talk any more. I will answer your questions, but I *won't* answer that question you asked me . . . I *won't!*

Gentlemen, have you any further questions at this stage which you would like me to put to this witness? No? Thank you. Mrs Bayford, you may stand down. We may want you again later.

Call Mary Elizabeth Lamort . . . What is it, sir? What is it? I cannot have you interrupting the Court in this way! If you have any business with the Court, please tell the clerk. In the meantime we are waiting for another witness . . . Call Mary Elizabeth Lamort.

I am Miss Lamort's doctor. I wish to make a statement.

Miss Lamort's doctor? Please come up to the table, sir.

IX

William Eustace Fothergill, M.R.C.S., L.R.C.P.

What is your full name?

My full name is William Eustace Fothergill.

You wish to make a statement to the Court?

Yes. I should point out, however, that I have no connection with the case except in so far as that one of the witnesses is a patient of mine.

Will you make this statement, whatever it may be, upon oath?

Most certainly I will.

Very well, then. Please take the oath.

I swear by Almighty God that what I shall say in evidence in this Court shall be the truth, the whole truth and nothing but the truth.

You are a qualified medical practitioner?

Yes. I am a member of the Royal College of Surgeons and a licentiate of the Royal College of Physicians.

And you are medical adviser to . . .

Miss Mary Elizabeth Lamort.

And it is in connection with Miss Lamort that you wish to make a statement?

Yes.

Will you please do so?

Yes. It is my considered opinion that Miss Lamort—to put the matter into words easily apprehended by a layman—is in a nervous condition of such acuteness that it would be highly dangerous for her to be exposed at present to the ordeal of giving her evidence in this painful and distressing case.

That is your considered opinion?

I never express an opinion, sir, which is not considered. I

should perhaps add, however, that Miss Lamort has asked me to explain that she very much desires to give her evidence. In fact, she endeavoured to go contrary to my advice and return to Court from the waiting-room in which she is at the moment lying down. Fortunately, however, I prevailed upon her—

Quite, quite. How soon, Dr Fothergill, do you think that Miss Lamort will be in a condition to give her evidence without undue danger to her health?

That, Mr Coroner, is very hard to say. Miss Lamort has prevailed upon me, however, to allow her to come into Court and give evidence in an hour's time, *provided* that she is in a less acute nervous condition.

Miss Lamort, sir, has been my patient for three or four years. As you know, she is an actress—perhaps the greatest actress we have today. She brings to life the same emotional intensity which she brings to her art. She is, in fact, of an extraordinarily highly strung, neurotic disposition. The terrible event which is the subject of this inquiry has so disordered her nervous system that her condition is a matter for serious consideration. If you like, I will explain her condition in technical terms, but I doubt if this would be of any use.

Quite, quite! I take it, Dr Fothergill, that we will leave the matter like this. If she is able, Miss Lamort will give her evidence in an hour, or if we adjourn for the day before that time has elapsed we will leave her evidence until tomorrow.

Thank you, Mr Coroner.

Call Peter Joliffe Hargreaves.

X

PETER JOLIFFE HARGREAVES

WHAT is your full name?

Peter Joliffe Hargreaves.

Will you please take the oath?

I swear by Almighty God that what I shall say in evidence in this Court shall be the truth, the whole truth and nothing but the truth.

You are Peter Joliffe Hargreaves and your permanent residence is—?

Monk's Court, Storton Magna, Dorset.

You are an old friend of the Brunton family's?

I have been acquainted with the family for a considerable number of years.

You were a guest of the deceased, staying under his roof at the time of his death?

Yes.

You have heard the evidence of the preceding witnesses, including that of Mrs Bayford?

Yes.

Now, Mr Hargreaves, will you please tell us whether you can corroborate the evidence of Mrs Bayford as to when you last saw Mr Maxwell Brunton alive?

Certainly. He came into the drawing-room just after eleven.

You did not see him again?

No.

And when, Mr Hargreaves, you said good-night to Mrs Bayford in the corridor, you went straight into your room?

Yes.

Did you leave your room again that night at any time between your entering it and your being roused with the news of Mr Brunton's death?

No.

Did you go to bed?

Yes. Almost immediately I got to my room. I was very tired.

You heard no unusual noises of any kind in the house? Or any noise whatsoever?

None. I was asleep almost as soon as I got into bed.

I see. Thank you. Now, Mr Hargreaves, kindly tell the Court what your profession is.

I am a qualified physician and surgeon but do not practise.

You are, I suppose, of independent means?

Yes. I served throughout the war as a doctor in the R.A.M.C. in France, getting my commission as soon as I was qualified in 1915. After leaving the army in 1920 I started a private practice. I was in private practice for four years. Then my uncle, Sir Charles Hargreaves, died and left me his money and his house and estate in Dorsetshire. I gave up my practice and devoted my time to the estate.

Thank you, Mr Hargreaves, but we understand that you have been for a long holiday, only just recently, abroad. Is that so?

It is.

Will you please tell the Court the exact period for which you were abroad and where you have been. I am sorry, Mr Hargreaves, if my questions seem inapposite, but in matters of this kind all facts have to be collected.

I can understand that. I went abroad two years ago last May. I went first to South Africa to stay with my brother in Rhodesia. I was there for six months. I then went on a long hunting trip across what used to be 'German East,' and I was there for the rest of the time—that would be about fourteen months. My trip home took up the remaining four months of the two years I have mentioned.

Mr Hargreaves, was it your original intention to come home when you did?

No. I had intended to get back to South Africa and put in another visit to my brother.

What caused you to alter your mind?

The news which I read in an old paper of the death of Mrs Bayford's husband.

I see . . . I wonder whether we may assume, Mr Hargreaves, that Mrs Bayford's marriage was the cause of your leaving England?

You may. The assumption is correct.

And immediately you heard the news of the death of Mrs Bayford's husband, you decided to return home?

Yes. I hoped very much that Mrs Bayford would eventually consent to be my wife.

I see. On your return I suppose you immediately let Mrs Bayford know your whereabouts, and that was the cause of your being invited—at Mrs Bayford's insistence, as we have already heard from her evidence—to stay at Rajah Gardens?

That is correct.

Your visit has lasted how long, Mr Hargreaves?

A fortnight today.

And are your feelings toward Mrs Bayford still the same, Mr Hargreaves, as they were when you broke off your travels in Africa to come back to England? I am sorry to have to ask you all these questions, but they are necessary.

If my feelings have changed at all they have merely intensified.

I see. So that you still hope . . .?

Exactly. I still hope that Mrs Bayford will consent to become my wife. It has been pure cowardice upon my part that I do not already know the answer to this question. Just now, in this chair, Mrs Bayford—through this cowardice of mine—was subjected to what must have been an intensely uncomfortable, to say the least of it, ordeal, I want publicly to apologise to her . . .

·   ·   ·   ·   ·   ·

Please! Please! I cannot in any circumstances have interruptions. Please continue, Mr Hargreaves.

There would not appear, sir, to be any need for me to go on further—in answer to your last question, I mean.

Perhaps you are right, Mr Hargreaves. The Court is to take it, then, that you are deeply in love with Mrs Bayford and wish to marry her, and that in all probability you will do so?

Yes.

You have heard all the previous evidence given to this Court, Mr Hargreaves?

Every word.

With particular reference to Mrs Bayford's evidence, is there anything in that evidence with which you disagree?

Nothing whatsoever.

Even, Mr Hargreaves, as to the cause of this dislike which Mr Brunton exhibited—to more than one witness—of your presence in the house?

No. I did not know of this attitude of Mr Brunton's until I came to this Court. Whatever it was, the only possible explanation for it could be that which Mrs Bayford put forward. That explanation is most highly probable. Mrs Bayford and her father were devoted to each other.

We may take it, then, Mr Hargreaves, that during your stay at Rajah Gardens your relations with Mr Maxwell Brunton were absolutely unmarked by any—er—er—awkwardness of any description?

You may.

You had no suspicion that Mr Brunton resented you or your presence in any way whatsoever?

He was far too good a host and generous-minded a man.

Thank you, Mr Hargreaves. Now, as you have told me that you have followed all the previous evidence, you must be aware that I have been inquiring into the possibility of Mr Maxwell Brunton's having conducted, during the time immediately prior to his death, an undiscovered intrigue with some woman at least temporarily under his roof?

Yes.

Very well, then! I shall now ask you what I have been asking every witness—if, Mr Hargreaves, such an intrigue had in fact been going on, whom would you select as the most likely partner to such an intrigue?

I'm sorry, sir, I can't possibly answer that question. Please consider my position. I was a guest of short standing in this house. Save for Mrs Bayford, I knew none of the family intimately. I certainly knew none of the family history or private affairs. I was not even aware, until I heard the evidence, that Mr Brunton had the reputation of being—er—unwise in his dealings with women. In the circumstances, how can I possibly answer such a question as that put to me? Any conjecture, I mean, would not be based on anything solid enough to be worth making.

I see. Thank you, Mr Hargreaves . . . You have nothing, I suppose, to add to this last answer, on consideration?

Nothing whatsoever.

Very well, then . . . Did you notice, Mr Hargreaves, throughout your visit any unusual atmosphere in the family circle?

I'm afraid my answer to this question must be the same as the last. Not knowing the family intimately, how can I possibly tell whether the atmosphere was usual or unusual?

Let me put my question in another form, Mr Hargreaves: Did you, as a visitor and a temporary member of the household, become aware, either upon the day preceding his death or at any other time, that Mr Brunton was in disagreement with—or had been quarrelling with—any member of the household?

No.

You are sure?

Certain.

Perhaps you could tell me, Mr Hargreaves, whether at any time during your visit and up to the time of his death Mr

Brunton appeared to you to be in any way upset or unlike himself?

So far as I knew him, no.

That is a considered answer, Mr Hargreaves?

It is.

Thank you. Unless the jury have any further questions which they would like me to put to you at this stage . . . You have not, gentlemen? Thank you. I think, Mr Hargreaves, we can ask you to stand down, at least for the present . . .

Call Jeannette Bokay . . . One moment—one moment! . . . Yes, Dr Fothergill?

I wish to inform you, Mr Coroner, that Miss Lamort having made a rapid recovery, I would be willing to let her now give her evidence.

I see. Thank you, Doctor . . .

Call Mary Elizabeth Lamort.

XI

Mary Elizabeth Lamort

What is your full name?

Mary Elizabeth Lamort.

Will you please take the oath?

Please speak up, Miss Lamort! I'm afraid your words are inaudible.

I swear by . . . Almighty God that what I shall . . . say in evidence . . . in this Court . . . shall be . . . shall be the truth, the whole truth and nothing but the truth.

Thank you. Now, Miss Lamort, I understand that you have been for some time a close friend of the Brunton family's?

Yes . . . Or rather, that is, Enid . . . that is, Mrs Brunton and I are old friends.

Did you say, Miss Lamort, that Mrs Brunton and you are old friends? I'm afraid I can't hear you very distinctly.

Yes, that was what I said.

I see. And you were staying at 44 Rajah Gardens on the night of the death of Mr Maxwell Brunton?

Yes.

I am sorry, Miss Lamort, but I am afraid I must ask you again to speak up. I can only just hear your replies myself, and the foreman has just told me that several members of the jury can hardly hear you at all.

My . . . my . . . Please may I have . . . My mouth's so dry.

Please take the witness a glass of water.

Thank you so much! There! I'm all right now.

Miss Lamort, when did you last see Mr Maxwell Brunton alive?

At the same time as the others. I was in the drawing-room.

He came in. If they say it was eleven, it must have been. I don't know the time. He stood and talked a little and went away. I never saw him again.

And you went to bed, Miss Lamort, at what time?

Again I'm afraid I don't know the time . . . But I went up with all the others.

According to the other witnesses it was approximately eleven-thirty. Is that in agreement with your recollection?

Yes . . . I suppose that must have been the time . . .

Did you go straight to your bedroom after leaving the draw-ing-room, Miss Lamort?

Yes.

Did you leave your bedroom again at any time between this and the time you were roused by Mr Harrison and the police sergeant?

No.

Did you hear any unusual noises during that time or any noises at all in the house?

.   .   .   .   .   .

Please speak up, Miss Lamort!

I'm sorry. No, I heard no noises—no unusual noises . . . There may—there may have been just a few sounds like doors shutting or—you know the sort of noise I mean—but that was only immediately after I went to my room . . . If there were any more . . . I don't suppose I should have heard them . . .

Do you mean, Miss Lamort, that you were in bed and asleep very soon after you retired?

Yes.

And the next thing you knew was that Mr Harrison and the police sergeant were knocking at your door?

Yes.

I see. How long, Miss Lamort, had you been staying in the house?

Let me see . . . about a fortnight . . . No, it was more . . . I'm sorry, I have no head for dates and things like that, and my

head's feeling so queer. I could find out if . . . No, I know—
wait . . . Three weeks exactly to—to—to—*that* day!

Were you a constant visitor at the house, Miss Lamort?

I had often been there before—but not to stay . . . You see,
I live in London, and so when I went there before it was just
in the afternoon or to dinner perhaps—that sort of thing.

*You had never stayed in the house before? Would you please
explain, Miss Lamort, how it was that you were actually living
in the house for this three weeks?*

Yes. My flat is being done up. I had been putting it off and
putting it off, and one day when I was having tea with Enid,
Mrs Brunton, I told her about it and she—she is always so
kind—she suggested that I should go and stay with her while—
while—until the decorators had finished my flat.

*I see. How long exactly have you known the Brunton family,
Miss Lamort?*

I've known Enid—Mrs Brunton—I should say, all my life . . .
We are second cousins . . . She used to be very nice to me when
she was at Girton and I was a little schoolgirl.

*And you kept up this friendship throughout the whole of the
intervening years?*

Yes.

*I suppose, then, Miss Lamort, that you knew Mr Maxwell
Brunton very well?*

Yes—I suppose, though, it all depends on what you mean
by 'very well.' It was Enid, of course, that I went to see . . . I
met Maxwell, of course, many times . . . but somehow I don't
think he liked me very much.

*Miss Lamort, I take it from your evidence that you were, as
well as a cousin and an acquaintance, an intimate friend of
Mrs Brunton?*

Yes.

*Did Mrs Brunton ever confide in you? Did she, I mean, ever
reveal to you any of the troubles she had with her husband in
regard to his various intrigues with other women?*

Never. Enid—Mrs Brunton—adores—adored Maxwell. Whatever she may have felt she would never, never, *never* have told anything to anyone . . . Never!

I see. But as a friend of Mrs Brunton's and a fairly constant visitor to the house I take it, Miss Lamort, that you must have been aware of Mr Brunton's unfortunate failing?

Only . . . only . . . vaguely. I mean, well, one hears things, of course, but I can't say that I ever . . . I always try not to listen . . . There's so much scandal and backbiting in the world that I've always done my best to keep myself away from all that sort of thing . . . It's very difficult, of course, in my profession, but . . .

I see. I think you mean, Miss Lamort, that while you naturally had heard remarks about Mr Brunton's infidelities, you had never taken much notice of them or their implication?

Yes, that's right.

It is now my painful duty, Miss Lamort, to ask you this question: Were you at any time on terms of intimacy with the deceased?

I . . . What do you mean! I've told you, I knew Maxwell just as Enid's husband . . . What do you *mean?*

If you wish me to put my question more clearly, Miss Lamort, I must ask you whether you were ever on terms of sexual intimacy with Mr Brunton.

My God! My God! . . . How *dare* you sit there and ask *me* . . . and put me your foul questions! . . .

Am I to take it that your answer is in the negative, Miss Lamort?

You are! No, no, and *no!*

Can you explain to the Court how, then, although you were on merely acquaintanceship terms with Mr Brunton, as you have told the jury, yet you have obviously experienced such a terrible shock in the matter of his death?

.   .   .   .   .   .

Please get Miss Lamort another glass of water.

.   .   .   .   .   .

Are you feeling sufficiently recovered, Miss Lamort, to answer my question, or would you prefer that I call Dr Fothergill to give an opinion as to whether you should have a respite?

No! No! I'll go on. Ask your question.

I must repeat my last question—why is it that, although you say you were not even on very friendly terms with Mr Maxwell Brunton, his death has caused you so obviously great a shock?

How could I tell you? Some people have their feelings, their nerves, their souls under restraint—restraint, restraint, always restraint! Some people are so like that, that even if the world were to come to an end under their feet they would still *smile* and talk silly small talk! . . . I am not like that—I'm not! I'm *not*! . . . I live on my nerves . . . I hate death! I loathe death! I am terrified, terrified of death! And then in that quiet house death comes and leers at all of us! . . . How can I help . . . How could I help . . . I thought I should die too!

You are meaning us to understand, Miss Lamort—I am sorry to keep harping on this question—you are meaning us to understand that it was the fact of the death and the way it had come about that so seriously shocked you? The fact and not the subject?

Yes. Put it any way you like. You know what I mean.

I see. We have nearly come to an end, now, Miss Lamort. One question which I want to put to you now is this: Did you, in your stay in the house, notice any particularly strained atmosphere among the family or observe that Mr Brunton was in any way unlike himself? I want you to answer this question with reference to your whole stay and particularly with reference to the day preceding his death.

No, I noticed nothing unusual at all . . .

You have considered that answer, Miss Lamort?

Yes.

Has any member of the jury any further questions which he wishes me to put to this witness? . . . Thank you, Miss Lamort. You may stand down.

Call Jeannette Bokay.

XII

Marie Jeannette Bocquet

What is your full name?

Your pardon, m'sieu?

I said what is your full name?

My *full* name?

Yes, yes—your first name and your second name.

Oh, pardon, m'sieu! My name they are Marie Jeannette Bocquet.

Thank you. Now, Mamzel Bokay, will you please take the oath?

Pardon, m'sieu? I do not understand.

Will you swear on the Bible, mamzel, that what you say in evidence here shall be truthful?

Certainement, m'sieu. Why should I not swear? I never lie, me! I am 'ere to say the truth. How would it serve? . . .

Thank you . . . Please hand the witness the Book and show her the form of oath.

I swear by the Almighty God that what I shall say in *évidence* in this . . . this Court shall be the truth, the 'ole truth and nosing but the truth.

Your full name is Marie Jeannette Bokay and you are employed as lady's maid to Mrs Maxwell Brunton?

But yes, that is certain.

You are not a newcomer to the Brunton household?

Pardon, m'sieu?

You have not just recently taken up your duties as lady's maid to Mrs Brunton?

Oh no, m'sieu. I have been with Madame a long, long time. I 'ope that I 'ave give'—

Thank you, mamzel. That will do at the moment. Now then:

Were you in the house on the night of the death of Mr Maxwell Brunton?

But certainly, m'sieu! I 'ave tol' the gendarme not once but . . . two 'undred time.

Yes, yes! But what you have told the police has not at the moment anything to do with this Court, Mamzel Bokay.

Oh!

Now, Mamzel Bokay, will you please tell the jury what time you last saw your employer alive.

Yes, m'sieu, I last see 'im at half-past after eleven on Thursday night. I have just finished—

One moment, Miss Bokay, one moment! If I look at the police notes which I have here I find that you said to the police that you last saw Mr Brunton at five minutes past eleven. Will you please explain the discrepancy between that statement and the one you have just made?

You mean, m'sieu, how was it that I say one thing Thursday night and another now? It is that since I talk to the officer I was—how do you call it?—all of a dither. After, when I think, I remember that it was at half-past after eleven that I last see M'sieu Broonton. I am coming out of Madame's room, and I see M'sieu Broonton just going into the study. I think that he has just been to she bathroom.

Did Mr Brunton speak to you?

Non, m'sieu, he did not speak. Mr Broonton and I, we did not speak much, you see.

You saw Mr Brunton, then, entering the study? Did he close the door behind him?

Yes, m'sieu.

And that was the last time you ever saw him alive?

Yes, m'sieu.

At what time, Mamzel Bokay, did you yourself go up to your room to bed?

At that time I tell you, m'sieu. At that time I was coming out of Madame's room and I see M'sieu Broonton going into the study. I am then, you see, going to my bed. I go at once to my bed, and I go to sleep also at once.

I see. And that is all you knew, Mamzel Bokay, until your awakening by Mr Harrison and the police sergeant?

Yes, m'sieu. Ah, it is 'orrible, that—'orrible. that! I hear the boom, boom, boom, on the door. I think it is just a dream, and then it continue, boom, boom, boom, like that, and I wake—

That will do, Mamzel Bokay. I want you just to answer my questions.

I see, m'sieu, pardon!

Now, Mamzel Bokay, you say that you went straight to bed and straight to sleep; that you were on your way up to bed when you saw Mr Brunton at eleven-thirty and therefore you must have been in bed and asleep, shall we say, about a quarter to twelve?

That is right, m'sieu.

And you were not awakened from your sleep until the arrival of Mr Harrison and the police sergeant?

That is right, m'sieu.

Now, Mamzel Bokay, please call to mind as fully as you can the quarter of an hour that elapsed after your leaving Mrs Brunton's room—and seeing Mr Brunton at the door of his study—and the time when you got into bed.

Yes, m'sieu, I remember the time. I do not forget, I!

During that quarter of an hour, Mamzel Bokay, did you hear any unusual sounds in the house?

Non, m'sieu.

Did you hear any sound at all in the house?

Oui, m'sieu. Yes, I hear doors open and shut; I do not hear any voices, just doors open and shut.

But that was a normal noise in the household at that time?

Yes, m'sieu.

You heard nothing else?—no voices, for instance?

Non, m'sieu.

Thank you. Now perhaps you will tell these gentlemen and

myself, first, how long you had been in service with Mrs Brunton, and second, what your duties were?

But certainly, m'sieu. I have been with Madame now one, two, let me see, four years not quite. What I have to do, it is to be lady's maid to Madame, and also I have—it is *extraordinaire* this, but there is not the place in the house for another servant, so that is why—what I have to do is to be lady's maid to Madame and to give my help in some of the work like, you see, the making of the beds; the looking out, the how do you say, linen, and, oh, how shall I say?—you know, all like that . . . that . . .

I quite understand . . . During your four years in the house, did you find Mrs Brunton a good mistress to work for?

Ah, *oui*! . . . But yes, m'sieu! Yes, yes.

You were happy in your work there?

Yes, I am happy to work for Madame. I was not always happy all over, but what is that?

Now, Mamzel Bokay, you have heard the evidence given by the other witnesses—

Yes, m'sieu, I have heard what the people who come and sit here where I sit—I have heard what they all say. *Mon Dieu*, have I not heard what they say! and have I not thought; *le Bon Dieu, il—*

Please just answer my questions: if there are any other statements you wish to make, you will have an opportunity to do so later on. Now, then: if you have heard the evidence of all the other witnesses, you must have heard that of Mr Adrian Brunton—

Mon Dieu, ce—

Mamzel Bokay! I had not yet reached my question. In evidence Mr Adrian Brunton made a statement to the effect that you had been on—er—intimate terms with Mr Maxwell Brunton. Is that statement correct?

M'sieu, je regarde ce salle . . . Oh, I must speak in English. I am sorry. M'sieu, I have heard what that Adrian he say. I have heard and I have just wait, wait, wait, until this time! M'sieu, what Adrian he say, it is true, *mais je ne pense pas—*

Please calm yourself, and I am afraid I must ask you not to break into your own language. I can realise how difficult it must be to speak under circumstances like this in a foreign tongue, but still, since you can speak English, I must ask you to do this. Now let us continue. I understood you to say just now that you corroborate Mr Brunton's evidence, that is to say, you agree that at some time you were intimate with Mr Brunton—you realise what I mean?

Parfaitement. I understand perfectly. I know all that it means—all! I say to myself before I come here today to this place: J'n'ette, how do you do if all this—all this—what you have just say, m'sieu, all this is to—what do you call it?—come out. And at first, m'sieu, at first I say to myself: J'n'ette, you say no, no, no; you say that it is not true. Then I think to myself, m'sieu, but wait! For I think: there is M'sieu Broonton who has been kill', and I think this is *une affaire sérieuse*—a thing which is very great—a thing in which a girl must not say anything but that which is the truth; and I think—

One moment! Will you please condense your answers—make them a little shorter. All this court is concerned with at present is whether you can corroborate, that is, whether you agree with, the evidence of Mr Adrian Brunton. I take it that you do. I understand that you admit yourself that you were at one time on terms of full intimacy with Mr Maxwell Brunton?

Yes, m'sieu.

At what time was this? At what period? When?

It is all right what that Adrian he say. All right except—

One moment. You agree with Mr Brunton's assumption of the time when this liaison was taking place—that is, about eighteen months ago?

Yes, m'sieu.

Can you give us any more exact time?

That time, a year and half a year—he is right.

And how long did this affair continue?

Ah, m'sieu, it was not a long time; it was a very short time. It was perhaps because I was—how do you say?—a silly damfool girl, but M'sieu Broonton he was, how do you say, 'ansome, so *magnifique*, so— Oh, 'ow I wish I could explain 'im. It does not matter. I was a silly damfool girl. That is what matters. I—

You can give us, then, no clearer notion of how long the—er—affair actually went on for? Was it a month, or two months, or more?

Ah, *non*, m'sieu, not even one month it was. Perhaps a week, I do not know; perhaps two weeks, but not a month, m'sieu! And, m'sieu—

One moment. I take it that Mr Adrian Brunton was correct when he stated that no one else in the house except you and his father and himself knew of this affair?

But, m'sieu, evidently.

Yes, yes, I see. Mamzel, what were your feelings for Mr Maxwell Brunton after he terminated your intimacy?

Pardon, m'sieu. I do not quite understand what you say now.

I am asking you to tell the Court what your feelings were after Mr Brunton had, to put it plainly, got rid of you; put an end, that is, to the affair?

M'sieu Broonton make an end to the affair! *Mr Broonton!* . . . M'sieu, that is what I have been waiting for. That Adrian—it cannot hurt me, what I say now, for after this, how can I stay with Madame?—that Adrian, he lies! Lies, lies, lies! He, that Adrian—that Adrian—he—how do you say?—make it look—make it seem, that M'sieu, his father, he chuck me off. That, m'sieu, is not true. It is a lie, a damn lie! What happened, m'sieu, is like this. After this little time—a week, two weeks, it is me who understand. I think, think, think, think; it is me who understand that this is—not right. Not right for me, not right for Madame. It is I, m'sieu, J'n'ette Bocquet, who make the end. If it had not been I to make the end, how could I, m'sieu, have—

One moment. I am sorry to interrupt you, but I must confine you just to answering my questions. To put it in a few words, I gather that your answer to my last question is that, though you admit a liaison with Mr Maxwell Brunton, it was a short liaison, lasting no more than a week or two, and finally that it was terminated by you of your own volition.

Pardon, m'sieu. I do not understand that last word you say.

I was saying that you stated that the affair was ended by you and not by Mr Brunton.

That is right, m'sieu.

Now, Mamzel Bokay, the Court will have to hear from your own lips whether this liaison with Mr Maxwell Brunton was ever resumed after it was broken off.

Pardon, m'sieu?

I think you understand what I mean. I am asking you whether you ever had any further *intimacy with Mr Brunton?*

Aftaire I finished, *non*, m'sieu, *non, non*, nevaire! I would not do that, I!

You are sure?

Mais certainement! But yes, m'sieu!

When you told us just now, Mamzel, that eleven-thirty was the last time on that night that you saw Mr Brunton, and that then you did not speak to him, and that then he was just entering his study, were you satisfied that that is the truth and the whole truth?

Yes, m'sieu!

Very well. We will leave that point now . . . I will ask you whether you know of any other liaison which Mr Brunton may have had with any woman living in the house which was still continuing up to the time of his death. Do you understand me?

Perfectly, m'sieu. I, I do not know. M'sieu Broonton, *il adore les*—I am sorry, m'sieu, I wish to say M'sieu Broonton, he cannot stay away from the ladies—cannot, cannot, cannot! And the ladies, I know, they cannot stay away from M'sieu Broonton. He is so 'ansome, he is so *jeune homme* . . . But you ask, m'sieu, whether I know of any othaire little *affaire* up to just this time now. I do not know; how can I know? I am not—I do not even talk with M'sieu Broonton. But if you look, m'sieu, how could it be? There is not one in the house. Ma'mselle Lamort, she is, how you say, very lovely, but she is a lady who is—well, she is cousin to Madame, and she is great friend to Madame, and she is, how you say, cold, cold! No, m'sieu, I do not—

Very well; I take it that you cannot give us any help in this matter. Now, then, another question: Did you, during the time immediately before Mr Brunton's death, and particularly during the day preceding his death, notice anything unusual about the atmosphere of the household? I mean, did there seem to be a strained atmosphere? These quarrels which we have heard of between Mr Brunton and members of his family, did they show themselves to persons outside the family such as yourself? I hope you understand me?

Perfectly, m'sieu. I shall say: Yes.

Indeed! Perhaps you will tell us some of the things you noticed?

Yes, m'sieu. The first time I notice, it is Madame. I have been maid to Madame a long time. I *know* Madame, and on that day Madame is—well—she is distracted.

By distracted, what do you mean exactly? Was she—did you see her weeping? Or did her nerves seem to give way or . . . could you explain yourself a little more fully?

I mean, m'sieu, that Madame, she give way that day. She is *très, très jalouse.* In 'er room, she walk up down, up down. She will not speak to J'n'ette. She will not speak to anyone. But she speak all the time to 'erself.

When did you first notice this behaviour of Mrs Brunton's?

M'sieu, M'sieu 'Arrison, he tell you, 'ow shall I say, of the quarrel between M'sieu and Madame. It was aftaire that. Madame she go straight to 'er room. I was there seeing to Madame's clothes. She do not mind me. She is used to J'n'ette. She take no notice, but she walk, as I tell you, up down, up down, up down! And she does not speak except always to 'erself.

May I ask whether you had ever seen Mrs Brunton behave in a similar manner before?

But yes, m'sieu. Not once, not twice, but many, many time'.

Can you give us definite information, Mamzel, as to when these other occasions were? I mean, can you give us dates and times?

M'sieu, 'ow can I do that? I am not, what do you say, a cullender. I am not a book for other people to write in. But often, yes, Madame do like this.

If you cannot tell us dates, perhaps you would be able to tell us about these other occasions when you had seen Mrs Brunton behaving in this way. Did they, to your knowledge, coincide with her having had trouble with Mr Brunton?

But of course, m'sieu. Why else should Madame go like this? Talk to 'erself. Walk up down, up down?

You are not speaking from conjecture, Mamzel?

Pardon, m'sieu. I do not quite understand what you say.

You are telling us, Mamzel, what you know, *not what you guess?*

But, m'sieu, should I come into this place 'ere and tell just what I guess! Ah, *non*! I tell only 'ere what I know.

I see. On this particular day—on last Thursday, Mamzel, how long did this behaviour on Mrs Brunton's part continue?

But, m'sieu, 'ow can I know? I attend to Madame. I see Madame like this. I know that Madame does not wish that anyone shall see her like this. I attend to Madame's clothes, and I go. It is not possible for me to say what you ask.

I see. When, Mamzel, after this incident did you next see Mrs Brunton?

I cannot say, m'sieu. I see Madame all day, all day! I am not a clock. How can I say?

If you cannot say when, *perhaps you could tell us whether, when next you saw Mrs Brunton, she appeared to have recovered?*

But certainly, m'sieu. When next I see Madame she is joost the same as she is always.

Did this strike you as strange in any way?

But *non*, m'sieu. That is so like Madame. Joost when she is alone—she does not count J'n'ette—she, how you say, let go. But soon, very soon, she is joost the same Madame that everyone see always.

You cannot add anything to your statement in regard to this behaviour on Mrs Brunton's part on Thursday last?

Non, m'sieu. If there is anything else which I 'ad to say, I should 'ave tol' you.

I see . . . A little while ago, I see from my notes—in fact, at the beginning of your evidence—you began to make some sort of a statement in regard to the evidence of the other witnesses. Do you follow what I am saying?

But perfectly, m'sieu.

You remember the incident to which I refer?

Remember! I 'ave been waiting!

This reference of yours which I cut short to keep you confined to answering my questions seemed to imply, if I am not mistaken, that you did not agree with all the evidence that you have heard?

M'sieu, that is so, beyond all doubt.

Would you like to amplify that statement, Mamzel?

Pardon, m'sieu. I do not quite—

Would you like to tell me in your own way exactly what it was in what any of these other witnesses said with which you do not agree?

Ah, m'sieu. Would I *like*! I come here to tell the truth, I! and when I sit there and sit there and sit there, joost waiting until it is J'n'ette's turn, and I 'ear what they all say, these people, and then I—

Please confine yourself to making any statement you have to make. I understand that you disagree with some of the evidence you have heard. I asked you to make a statement, but I am afraid that you are wandering off on to other matters . . . Perhaps it would be better if I asked you questions . . . Have you, for instance, anything to say in disagreement with the evidence of Mr Harrison?

Ah, *non*, m'sieu! M'sieu 'Arrison, what does *'e* mattaire? 'E is the little gentleman who, 'ow do you say, lick the envelopes for M'sieu. 'E talk a lot 'ere, but that is, I t'ink, because he does not often get a chance to talk.

Do you disagree with anything in the evidence of Mrs Brunton?

But no, m'sieu. Madame—when Madame speak it is the truth. She does not speak to you very many words, but what she *do* speak, that is true.

Do you disagree with anything in the evidence of Mr Adrian Brunton in any respect other than that which you have already told us?

Pardon, m'sieu, but I do not quite understand. You speak so quick, and you use words very difficult.

I was asking whether there was anything in Mr Adrian Brunton's evidence that you disagree with. Anything, that is, beyond the question of who it was that stopped the alliance between you and Mr Maxwell Brunton. That we have already gone into in your evidence. Do you understand me now?

But perfectly, m'sieu. No. In what that Adrian he say, there is nothing else which I can say it is not true.

Do you disagree with anything in the evidence of Mrs Bayford?

But m'sieu, *yes*. I wait and I wait, and at last you come!

Is it that you disagree with Mrs Bayford's evidence in general or in any particular?

Pardon, m'sieu. I do not understand.

Is it with one thing that you disagree—?

Yes, m'sieu. One thing, but what a big thing! . . . It is what Madame Bayfoot she say about M'sieu Broonton and M'sieu 'Argreave'. Madame Bayfoot, she try to make you t'ink that the *raison* for M'sieu Broonton not to like M'sieu 'Argreave' is joost because M'sieu 'Argreave' 'e may want to marry Madame Bayfoot and take Madame Bayfoot away from M'sieu Broonton. That it is wrong. It is a lie! That is not the *raison*. It may be a little of the *raison*, but not all. No! The *raison* M'sieu Broonton not like M'sieu 'Argreave' is because, a long time ago, M'sieu Broonton 'e 'ave liaison with Madame 'Argreave' who is that M'sieu 'Argreave's mother. I do not tell things, but this is—*une affaire grande sérieuse*. I tell what I know. M'sieu Broonton, he has been killed and everything should—how do you say?—come out . . . M'sieu, when M'sieu Broonton, when I and M'sieu Broonton were *intime*, M'sieu Broonton, 'e tell me many thing. 'E tell me once that the only thing 'e is sorry in the whole of his life, it is the one woman who 'e love. She killed 'erself. That is aftaire the amour. He tell me that this woman is the mother of *le jeune homme* who at one time it was possible Madame Bayfoot should marry. He tell me that while it was possible that Madame Bayfoot wish to marry this—*fils*— son of this so foolish woman who kill 'erself, then it was very sad, very *difficile* for M'sieu Broonton. He tell me that it was all right after because Madame Bayfoot she did not marry this son. She marry M'sieu Bayfoot instead. M'sieu Bayfoot, M'sieu Broonton say, is a rotter! But M'sieu Bayfoot die, so everyt'ing, he say, in the garden was lovely. That, of course, m'sieu, was before M'sieu 'Argreave' he come back from Afrique. M'sieu Broonton, 'e tell me also that while it was possible that M'sieu 'Argreave' should wish to marry Madame Bayfoot when she was Mademoiselle it was very *difficile* for M'sieu Broonton because he always—'ow do you say?—wonder, wonder when M'sieu 'Argreave' will find out. 'E sometimes t'ink that perhaps M'sieu 'Argreave' will find out, and then 'e will come back and there will be—*fracas*. I tell you, m'sieu, that when Madame Bayfoot and M'sieu 'Argreave' sit in this chair and they tell you what they tell you I could not hardly but speak. It is not true! It is not right that they should sit in this chair and tell you lie!—that M'sieu Broonton did not like M'sieu 'Argreave' just because M'sieu 'Argreave' might marry Madame Bayfoot. I tell you, m'sieu—

One moment, please, one moment.

But, m'sieu, I 'ave not—

One moment, please! You must remember that it is rather

difficult for us to follow evidence given by someone not fully conversant with the language.

Pardon, m'sieu, I do not quite—

Never mind, never mind. I should like to ask you whether I have understood correctly. I have understood you to say that you believe the reason for Mr Maxwell Brunton's dislike of having Mr Hargreaves in his house to be on account of Mr Hargreaves's mother having committed suicide—killed herself—following an illicit love affair—a liaison, you understand—with Mr Brunton?

That is right, m'sieu. That is what I say.

Now, Mamzel . . . a very—er—difficult—er—delicate question. I have to ask you whether you intend to suggest to the Court that the deceased Mr Maxwell Brunton was, in fact, the father of Mr Peter Hargreaves? . . .

Silence! I must insist upon silence in the court-room!

Now, Mamzel, you heard my question?

Parfaitement, m'sieu. You say is it that M'sieu 'Argreave' is really the child of M'sieu Broonton? . . . Non, non, non. I do not mean that . . . that . . . that . . . It is not so! At the time when M'sieu Broonton 'e was—'ow do you say?—'aving an affair with Madame 'Argreave', this M'sieu 'Argreave' 'e was already—'ow do you say?—schoolboy. Non, m'sieu, all I say is that the *raison* that M'sieu Broonton 'e does not like M'sieu 'Argreave' is not only that 'e does not want Madame Bayfoot to go from 'im and marry M'sieu 'Argreave' but it is also that M'sieu Broonton 'e is afraid that M'sieu 'Argreave' 'e will find out that 'is mother make death for 'erself because of M'sieu Broonton. That is all I say, for all that I say 'ere is the truth only.

This is an amazing story, Mamzel. Have you any means of substantiating it?

Pardon, m'sieu, I do not—

I beg your pardon. I mean, have you anything to show which will prove *what you say? Can you understand that?*

But perfectly, m'sieu. It is only when you use those words

so strange, so *difficile*, and I do not understand. *Oui*, m'sieu. Yes. You ask me if I 'ave anyt'ing to show. What do I do! I open my bag—so! I take out this little package—so! I hand the package to this gentleman with the kind face and I ask 'im to give it to you. Inside the packet you will find a lettaire which is a lettaire written from this *pauvre* Madame 'Argreave' to M'sieu Broonton. The lettaire which M'sieu Broonton he give me when he tell me all the—what do you say?—yarn. If M'sieu will—

One moment, please. One moment.

. . . .

Thank you, sir. All you gentlemen have seen this letter? . . . Mamzel Bokay, will you please inform this Court how you came into possession of this document which you have just handed in to the jury?

This—this—how do you say, m'sieu?

Come, come. This letter—this letter here. How did you get hold of it?

But, m'sieu, I tell you! M'sieu Broonton give me this lettaire when he tol' me the whole—what do you call it?—yarn.

That is your considered statement?

Pardon, m'sieu. I do not quite understand what you say.

When you tell me that Mr Maxwell Brunton actually told you this story and gave you this letter, are you serious? Do you mean me to take this as your serious evidence? I hope that is clear.

But, m'sieu, perfectly. But, m'sieu, I cannot understan' how you ask. I am here to tell you all I know. What I tell you is the truth. If I tell you M'sieu Broonton he—

Very well, very well. Can you give us any idea how it was that Mr Brunton told you these very intimate details of his past and showed you this letter—this damaging, incriminating letter?

But *m'sieu*, M'sieu Broonton, 'e was—how do you say?—'e love' me. 'E tell me anyt'ing. M'sieu Broonton would 'ave gone on loving me, but, as I tell you, I see that it is wrong, and I stop. But while M'sieu 'e love me, 'e tell me *everyt'ing*.

I see. I see. Now, is there anything else that you have to tell us in this connection? That is to say, now we understand what you have said and have read this letter which you have handed in, is there any further evidence you have to give in connection with this particular point? You follow me?

Perfectly, m'sieu. I 'ave nothing further to say. I 'ave tell you all I know, and I 'ave tell you the truth. That is all.

Do you mean to say, that is all you have to tell in regard to the evidence of the other witnesses you have heard?

Non, m'sieu. There is one other t'ing that you 'ave not ask' me.

But I have asked you. There is no other witness.

But, m'sieu, you 'ave not ask' me about the man Jenning' and what 'e say.

Jennings? Oh, well, well! Perhaps you are right. Have you anything . . . What is it that you have to say?

I 'ave tol' you, m'sieu, I come 'ere aftaire I 'ave think, think, think, and—how do you say?—I decide that, in this *affaire grande sérieuse,* I must say everyt'ing . . .

About this Jennings, Mamzel?

I think I should tell you that this man Jenning' 'e is *félon*—how do you say?—'e 'as been in prison. 'E—what is it?—made getaway. 'E is—

One moment. One moment. Are you trying to tell the Court that Jennings, Mr Maxwell Brunton's butler, is an escaped convict?

Convic'. That is it. That is the word. Yes, m'sieu, 'e is convic', and 'e is, ah! I 'ave it, escape'.

But, good gracious me, girl! Really your evidence . . . Have you—how do you come to know this? Please tell the Court at once what you mean by this extraordinary statement.

M'sieu est dérangé? I say what I say. I do not *think.* The thing that is not truth, I do not say. But I can give you—'ow do you say?—proof.

You mean seriously to tell me, Mamzel, that you have proof that this Jennings is a convict—criminal—and has escaped from prison?

But yes, m'sieu. That is what I tell you.

How do you come to know this astonishing—

But, m'sieu. It was, of course, M'sieu Broonton 'oo tell me. 'E tell me that Jenning' is, ah, yes, recommend' to 'im by a friend of 'is 'oo tell 'im to give Jenning' a chance because Jenning' is *un homme extraordinaire.* Jenning' is—what do you say, m'sieu?—an escape' convic', and Jenning' wish to 'ave a try-to-go-straight. So M'sieu Broonton, he take Jenning'.

But can you prove *this?*

M'sieu, there is no need for me to proof. All that is wanted is for you to tell the—the—police and ask them and say, This Jenning', is 'e an escape' convic'?

Yes . . . yes . . . I need not tell you, I suppose, that if these statements you are making are not true, you are liable to get yourself into serious trouble.

But, of course, m'sieu. I am not *folle*, I.

Well . . . I think . . . Is there anything else *which you wish to say?*

Oui, m'sieu. I 'ave not finish to tell you about Jenning'. It is not that I am unkind. It is that I wish to say the truth, and I know this, that Jenning', 'e steal from M'sieu Broonton, and that M'sieu Broonton, 'e find out that Jenning' steal from 'im.

When was this?

It was ago, not long. Let me think. *Un, deux, trois, quatre . . . Non*, it was one week ago. Jenning', 'e steal. 'E steal some money. M'sieu Broonton, 'e—how do you say?—find out. 'E did not find out on the day Jenning' steal, but he find out— *Merc*—Wednesday.

You mean the Wednesday immediately prior to his death?

That is right, m'sieu.

And Mr Brunton, when he found out, sent for Jennings? . . .

And 'e tell to Jenning', well, somet'ing that I do not know.

How do you know anything at all about this? You have told us that you and Mr Brunton no longer spoke together.

Ah, but, m'sieu, it is simple. I 'ear Jenning' and *cette grande vache*, that woman, 'is wife, I 'ear them talk. I can 'ear them. I do not listen. But they talk, they talk so loud they boom, boom, boom!

I see. You overheard a conversation between Jennings and his wife. Did you hear what Mr Brunton told Jennings he proposed to do about this?

But, m'sieu, I do not hear. I do not care. I do not listen. It is not my business.

I see. Is there anything else in any of the other evidence which you have heard about which you wish to make a statement?

No, m'sieu. It is just that I wish to speak the truth.

Mamzel Bokay, you have given some of the most astonishing evidence that as a coroner of many years' experience it has ever been my lot to hear. I want to ask you to reconsider this evidence. Will you please do so? Will you please, that is, think before you answer this question?—and then tell me whether you wish to change in any way any of your remarks and statements.

M'sieu, there is no reason for me to think. I only tell the truth. I do not change one word, *one word* of what I 'ave say.

One moment. Did Mr Maxwell Brunton himself tell you these things? That is, first about Mr Hargreaves's mother and second about Jennings? Or did you ascertain these things, first by, shall we say, finding *the letter which you have handed into Court, and second by* listening *to the conversation of Mr and Mrs Jennings?*

M'sieu. How many times have I got to say that I come here to tell the truth? I do not think it can be right for you to say such question. It is . . . it is not . . .

Very well. Will you please remain silent for a moment?

Gentlemen, you have just heard some astonishing evidence. I cannot but think, in view of this letter which we have read, that the witness has at least some foundation for part of her statements. I propose, if you agree, to ask this witness to stand down now—she seems to have finished at last—and proceed with the other evidence in the order which I had previously arranged. Of course, as you will have already realised, this is not a case in which my summing up will come after merely one hearing. So that there will be plenty of opportunity to go into the allegations made by Jeannette Bokay. I propose that we let this witness stand down without any further questions at this stage. I should remind you also, of course, that representatives of the police are now in Court and that they will pursue any line of inquiry which seems necessary to them outside this Court. Do you agree with my proposal, gentlemen? . . . Thank you very much.

Mamzel Bokay, you may stand down now. We may want to take further evidence from you again later.

Gentlemen, I will now go on with the other evidence as I had arranged . . . Call Sarah Jennings.

XIII

Sarah Margaret Ruby Jennings, Cook-Housekeeper to the Brunton Household

What is your full name?

Sarah Margaret Ruby Jennings.

Will you now please take the oath?

... I swear by Halmighty God that what I shall say in evidence in this Court shall be the truth, the 'ole truth and nothink but the truth.

You are Sarah Jennings and you are, I believe, employed as cook-housekeeper to the Brunton household?

I am that, sir.

How long have you held the position?

Two year come next October, sir.

And are you conversant, Mrs Jennings, with the general ways of the Brunton family?

That I am, sir. I've always been considered sufficient. I don't want to seem to be standing up 'ere a-blowin' of my own strumpet, but what I can do I knows I can do, and I 'aven't no shame in admittin'. I was engaged as a cook-'ousekeeper and I cooks well and I 'ousekeeps better. So that answers your question—you can't be a good cook no more than you can be a good 'ousekeeper—and certainly you can't be both—if you don't know the ways of the gentry that you're serving. There's far too many women goin' about—

Please, Mrs Jennings, you must let me speak! I'm afraid you misunderstood my last question. What I meant to ask you was this: Were you at all conversant with the relations of the Brunton family and their guests—er—one to the other?

I don't azackly quite see 'ow you mean, sir.

Dear me, we shall have to try again! What I am trying to get at is this, Mrs Jennings: being not only cook but housekeeper to the household it struck me that you must know their—how shall I put it?—their relations to one another: that you must know, in other words, of any particular friendships, dislikes, jealousies and that sort of thing.

Oh, I see what you mean, sir. Oh no, I know nothink o' that sort. I'm one as believes in bein' busy about my own work, not minding other folks' business—the which I might say doesn't seem to be the rule followed by a good many people whose names I might mention but for the sake of good manners will not do so. No, sir, I goes about me work and I does me work. So long as my employers are satisfied with me and treats me right and proper and befittin', as you might say, I'm satisfied. I never was one to 'old with a-introdoocin' foreigners into domestic service. Keep yourself to yourself, says I. And what I says to myself I keeps to. So if you was hopin' sir, with all due respect, as 'ow I should agree with all these other evidences what you've just twisted out, I beg to be allowed to state, sir, that you are in herror. I 'ave one rule in life and that is—

One moment, Mrs Jennings, one moment! In your position as cook-housekeeper did you frequently see the deceased?

Lor' bless me, no sir! Not 'alf so frequent as I should of liked, because if ever there was a real gentleman the master was that. Even now, sir, when I comes to think o' this 'orrible—

Did you happen to see Mr Maxwell Brunton, Mrs Jennings, upon the day preceding his death?

That I did not, sir, more's the pity! Why, a full week had gone by since I so much as set eyes on the master. Keep yourself to yourself is my motto. Not but what I shouldn't of liked to have seen the master, because, as I believe I says just now, a pleasanter, better gentleman never breathed than the master—

One moment, Mrs Jennings. Please, please! After all, I must be allowed to speak in this Court. I gather that the core of what you have been telling the jury is that you have nothing of any value whatsoever to add to the evidence which has gone before your own. That is, of course, in connection with those matters about which I have already asked you. Now, however, Mrs Jennings, coming to the point upon which you can help us—

Yes, sir. I know what you're goin' to say, sir. It's about Jennings. If I'd 'a' thought that little French tart—beggin' your pardon, sir, and you gentlemen all—but what else is a woman to call 'er?—If I'd 'a' thought that that Mamzelle, that pryin', snoopin', sneakin'—

Mrs Jennings, please! If you cannot restrain yourself I shall have to be rather more severe with you. Will you please answer my questions and do nothing else. We do not want your opinions, valuable though they doubtless are.

Yes, sir, I'm sure, sir, as I never meant any 'arm, sir. It all seemed so extr'ord'n'ry like.

Now, Mrs Jennings, I know already from the evidence of Jeannette Bokay, and also from corroboration which, a moment before you came on to the stand, I received from the police, that your husband, Arthur Waterloo Jennings, is an escaped convict; that when he escaped he was serving a term of three years' penal servitude at Parkmoor Prison on conviction for burglary. I know, too, that Jennings had served only a year of his sentence. What I do not know is whether Mr Brunton was aware of this when he first engaged you and your husband. Please spare us your further remarks about Bokay. We remember that she told us that Mr Brunton was aware of this. Will you now give us your answer?

Yes, sir. Mr Brunton didn't know, sir, when we took the places, but, sir, after we'd been with Mr Brunton a year and we'd seen, sir, what a fine master he was to work for, I sez to Jennings, I sez, we'd better tell 'im and get it over. You see, it 'ad been preying on my mind like. Jennings—'e cut up rough, but I settled *'im*, and the long and the short of it was that 'e

went to the master and 'e told 'im. As a matter of fack, I went
with 'im. We both seed the master. I wanted to keep me eye
on Arthur 'cause 'e might 'ave come back and sed 'e'd talked
to the master and not done nothink of the sort, not at all.
I mean, 'e's all right as men go, but that's not very far, is it? I
mean, *is* class of man, I wasn't speaking of the gentry, like
yourself, sir . . .

*So you mean to tell us, Mrs Jennings, that after a year of
service with Mr Maxwell Brunton, when you found out that he
was a generous and kindly master to work for you thought that
you must in duty bound tell him your secret? And that you and
your husband together, in fact, told him?*

Yes, sir, that's the truth. See it wet, see it dry! I'm sorry, sir;
I gets carried away sometimes. I meant to say that's the truth,
so 'elp me God! The truth, the 'ole truth, and nothink but the
truth.

I see, Mrs Jennings. That's the truth of the matter?

Yes, sir. It's as I said, sir. Jennings and me, after we'd been
there a year, well, we sez it's time that we went and saw the
master and told 'im. I didn't let 'im go 'imself, mind you.

*One moment, Mrs Jennings. I think you told us that before,
just now. Thank you. Now, Mrs Jennings—is there any foundation in fact—please consider your answer carefully before you
make it—is there any foundation in fact for Bokay's statement
that recently Jennings had stolen something from Mr Brunton?*

No, sir. Not from the master. Even Arthur wouldn't go for
to do that. It's a damn stinkin'—excuse me, sir, begging your
pardon—it's a dirty lie!

So that you have it, Mrs Jennings, that Bokay's story is false?

Well, I can't exactly say that, sir. You see, it was like this. One
day—it was in the middle of the month too, sir, and Jennings
and me was wanting to get rid of our old wireless set and get a
new one, sir—well, to cut a long story short, sir, it was like this:
Jennings, sir, was sent up by Sneaky Syd—I beg your pardon,
sir, I meant Mr 'Arrison—'e goes, sent up by Mr 'Arrison, to get

somethink or other from Mr 'Arrison's room, and while 'e's there, to cut a long story short, 'e sees some money on the dressing-table, and it so 'appens, the most peculiar thing, sir, to be just the amount of money we was wantin',' if you follow me, sir, sort of to make up what we wanted for this new radio set I was talking about. Well, Arthur, 'e sort of borrowed this money from Mr 'Arrison without sayin' anythink about it like. Mr 'Arrison found it out—I don't know 'ow—before Arthur 'ad 'ad a chance to pay it back, and Mr 'Arrison, 'e went and told the master, and the master, 'e sent for Arthur. I goes up with Arthur again, sir. I insisted like, not knowing what Mr 'Arrison may 'ave said. I never did trust that— Mr 'Arrison never was very popular with any of us. It's always been a myst'ry to us why the master used to keep such a—gentleman—about the place—

Now, Mrs Jennings! What did Mr Brunton say to you and your husband in this interview?

The master, sir, 'e said, sir, that 'e was considerin' what 'e was goin' to do about it, and 'e said, sir, 'e said as 'e'd let us know when 'e'd come to some decision, like. But we never 'eard, sir. The next week, the master . . . why, the master—

Come, Mrs Jennings, pull yourself together.

Do you mean to tell me that Mr Brunton never referred again to this very serious matter?

Well, sir, not refer exactly like. About a couple o' days arterwards Arthur *did* get a bit nervous and spoke to the master. But the master said as 'e 'adn't yet come to his decision like. 'E promised to let Arthur know the followin' Friday. But on the Wensday—on the Wensday . . .

Calm yourself, Mrs Jennings. Well, gentlemen, I think I have been through every point with this witness. I should suggest that there are no other matters on which she can be of use to us at present. Do you agree? . . . Thank you, Mrs Jennings, you may stand down . . .

Call Violet Ethel Burrage.

XIV

Violet Ethel Burrage, Kitchen Maid and Between Maid in the Brunton Household

What is your full name?

Violet Ethel Burrage.

Will you take the oath?

I thwear by almighty God that what I thall thay in evidenth in thith Court thall be the truth, the whole truth and nothing but the truth.

You are employed as scullery maid in the Brunton household?

No, thir. I was . . . I am kitthen maid and between maid, thir—

I see. I see. Well, Burrage, will you please tell the Court how long you have been employed in the Brunton household?

Yeth, thir. I have been there jutht about thirteen month, thir.

I see. Did you, Burrage, in the course of your duties frequently see the late Mr Maxwell Brunton?

Yeth, thir, and no, thir. I hardly know, thir, what you mean by frequently.

Burrage, there is no need for you to be nervous. Just imagine that you are answering a few questions that I am putting to you alone. Pay no attention to the rest of the Court.

I thee, thir. Thank you, thir.

That's right. Now then: let me put my last question to you in a slightly different form. How many times, on an average, would you say that you saw Mr Maxwell Brunton during a week?

I couldn't thay, thir. I uthed to thee the mathter nearly every day at one time or another.

I see. And you were fairly conversant, I suppose, with the ways of the household . . . By that, Burrage, I mean that you knew a good deal about the sort of life which was lived by the Brunton family?

Yeth, thir. I thuppothe tho.

Now, do you remember the day before Mr Brunton met his death?

Ye—ye—yeth, thir.

That was Wednesday last, wasn't it?

Ye—ye—yeth, thir.

Did you see Mr Brunton upon that day?

Ye—yeth, thir.

At what time did you see Mr Brunton upon that day?

At about midday, thir.

Are you sure of the time?

It wath *jutht* after twelve, thir.

And you didn't see him alive, again?

N—n—no, thir. *What were you doing at twelve noon upon Wednesday when you saw Mr Brunton?*

Pleathe, thir, the mathter wath in the library and hadn't thut the door, and I'd been putting away the thilver for Mithith Jenningth in the dining-room—

Yes. Very well, Burrage, we understand . . . Now, please tell the Court at what time you went to bed upon the Thursday night.

Early, thir. I'm thorry, I can't thay to a minute. But it mutht have been before ten, thir, becauthe I know I went up that night before Mithter and Mithith Jenningth, thir, and they're alwayth up by jutht after ten. They could p'r'apth tell you, thir, better than—

Yes, yes. Never mind that now. Let us say you were up in your room by 10 p.m. Your room is on the third floor, with the other servants?

Yeth, thir. Mithter and Mithith Jenningth have the room oppothite mine, thir, and Mith Bockey the one nektht.

And did you go to bed immediately you got to your room? . . . Please have patience, Miss Burrage.

I'm thorry, thir! Very thorry, thir! Only thereth thomething—thomething I ought to 'ave—ought to 'ave—

One moment, Burrage! Please let me conclude my questioning before you attempt to make any statement . . . I am going to ask you whether, between the time of your going to bed and your being wakened by Mr Harrison and the police sergeant, you heard any unusual noises in the house?

Thir, do you mean, thir, when I wath in my room or—

One moment, Burrage! Are you implying to the Court that after you went upstairs to your room you left it at any time in the night before you were finally wakened by the police sergeant and Mr Harrison?

Yeth, thir. That wath what I—

One moment, Burrage, one moment! What time did you leave your room?

I think it wath about half-patht one. Half-patht one wath what my clock thaid, thir, and it'th reliable.

What did you leave your room for at such a time?

I woke up with a thtart and remembered, thir, that I'd forgotten to turn off the tap in the linen room. The tap, thir, that cutth off the thteam from the hot pipe. The mithtreth ith very particular about that, thir, and I'm alwayth forgetting it, like. Tho when I woke with a thtart and remembered that I hadn't done it, I thought I'd betht get up and go down and thee, thir, at onth.

And you say that the time by your clock was then one-thirty?

Yeth, thir.

Now, to get back, Burrage. What was the noise that you heard while you were out of your room on this occasion?

I didn't hear a noithe, thir.

But I thought just now you were implying that you did?

I'm thorry, thir—I'm very thtupid, but pleathe, thir—

Look here, Burrage, I think the best thing you can do is to make this statement that seems to be on your mind in your own way. Please be as brief as you can. I assume it is something to do with what happened while you were either in the linen room— that is on the second floor, isn't it?—or on your way down to or up from it. Is that correct?

Yeth, thir. Pleathe, thir, I mutht thay—

Yes, yes. Go on!

I can only thay at the thtart that I hope I thhan't get into trouble. I can thee now that I ought to have made the politheman lithen to me when he wath athking uth all queththunth on Wenthday night. But thomehow, thir, I think I wath tho frightened like and upthet that I jutht anthered the queththunth he put to me, and I thought I'd jutht better wait until it came to be my turn to be the evidenth . . .

I see, Burrage. I see. Now, pull yourself together. There's no one to hurt you and nothing to be frightened of. If you tell what you know now, no harm will come to you.

I thee, thir. Thank you, thir. Thank you very much, thir. You want me to thay what I thaw, thir?

Yes, yes. Please go on.

Well, thir, it wath jutht ath I'd been in the linen room and turned off the thteam tap and wath coming out, opening the door very quietly tho ath not to make it thqueak and make a noithe that might wake anybody up—I wath jutht coming out when I did hear a little noithe, and I peeped round the corner of the cupboard, thir, and I thaw Mith Lamort.

Who? Who did you say? Speak up, please!

Mith—Mith—Mith Lamort, thir.

You saw Miss Lamort? And what was she doing?

Thir, the'd jutht come out of her room. She was jutht thutting the door.

What did she do? Did you watch?

Yeth, thir. It wathn't that I wanted to thpy, but I wath afraid I might get into trouble if the mithtreth knew that I'd left the tap on all that time; and the would have known if anyone had found that I wath in the cupboard, tho I jutht kept quiet, thir.

Yes, yes. But what did Miss Lamort do? Did you see?

Yeth, thir. The went along to the thtudy, thir.

She went along to the study, eh? How could you see all this?

Pleathe, thir, the landing light wath on. Mathter alwayth gave orderth that all the landing lighth thhould be left on. Not the pathage lighth, thir, but the landing lighth.

And this light makes it quite possible to see all the way down the corridor to the study?

Yeth, thir. Quite pothible.

What did Miss Lamort do when she reached the study?

Well, thir, the took hold of the handle and theemed to turn it very, very thlowly, and then at latht the opened the door and went in, thir.

Did the door shut, behind her?

Yeth, thir.

And what did you do then, Burrage?

Well, thir, I jutht went thwaight upthtairth to my room again and went back to bed.

I see. You know what the implication of your evidence is, of course?

Thorry, thir?

You understand in what direction your evidence is tending, don't you?

Yeth, thir. I only hope I than't get into trouble.

No, no, no. You've nothing to fear if you are telling the truth.

I alwayth tell the truth, thir.

What did you think, Burrage, when you saw Miss Lamort go into the study?

.   .   .   .   .   .

Speak up, please. I'm afraid we cannot hear you . . . I realise that this may be awkward for a respectable young girl like yourself, but I am afraid you will have to answer.

What did I think, thir? Only what I've alwayth thought in thith houthe—I wondered how people could be tho wicked . . .

You knew, then, Burrage, the sort of thing that used to go on in the house at times?

Yeth, thir. I'm not a fool, thir. Thometimeth I thought of giving notith, and then I thought well, after all, it'th nothing to do with me.

Yes, yes. Quite! So after you saw Miss Lamort enter the study you went back upstairs to your room and went to bed?

Yeth, thir. It wath a little while before I went to thleep, but I did get to thleep at latht.

And the next thing you knew was being wakened by Mr Harrison and the police sergeant?

Yeth, thir.

Now, Burrage, I want you to think very carefully before you answer this question. You are perfectly certain that it was Miss Lamort you saw?

Yeth, thir. There wath no one elth who'th tho tall with that beautiful hair, thir. And there'th no one elth in the houthe that would have that great green thtone. And bethide', thir, I know Mith Lamort. I couldn't make a mithtake like that. It would be impothible.

Yes, yes. Of course. How was Miss Lamort dressed?

.   .   .   .   .   .

Speak up, please!

The had on a nightdreth, thir.

What colour was it? Anything over it?

The nightdreth wath black, thir. I thould think it wath thilk. And the had jutht a thort of wrap over it, thir. Jutht a thin thing. Bright colourth on the front, thir—thome thort of embroidery.

Burrage, you said something about a green stone. I'm afraid I didn't quite follow you. Perhaps you would explain to the Court what it was you had in mind?

Oh, yeth, thir. Mith Lamort'th got a big thort of lovely thtone, thir. I don't know what ith called, the wearth it alwayth. I've never theen her without it. Ith a big green thtone and the wearth it round her neck.

Oh, I see—some sort of pendant. Thank you, Burrage. Now, did you hear any sounds after Miss Lamort had gone into the study and the door had shut behind her?

No, thir.

And you went straight upstairs again?
Yeth, thir.

.　　　　.　　　　.　　　　.　　　　.　　　　.

*I will have silence in this Court! Please keep quiet there!
Where's Dr Fothergill? . . . Doctor, can you have Miss Lamort
taken back to the waiting-room so that you can attend to her
there? . . . And, Doctor, she's not to be allowed to leave the Court.
Will she be fit soon to give evidence?*

My dear sir! I very, very, very much doubt whether Miss
Lamort will be fit to do anything—anything at all—for many,
many days. Perhaps weeks.

*Perhaps you will come back, Doctor, as soon as you can and
give us your report . . . SILENCE, please, in Court! SILENCE!*

*Now, Miss Burrage, perhaps we can get on! Have you heard
the evidence of all the other witnesses in this case?*

Yeth, thir.

*Leaving aside for the moment this one very important piece
of evidence which you have given us, is there anything in the
other previous evidences with which you disagree?*

No, thir.

*Gentlemen, I propose that at this stage we do not trouble this
witness any further. We can recall her if necessary but after this
extraordinary fresh line of inquiry which her evidence has opened
up, I think there would be no useful purpose in going over the old
ground, so that if there are no further questions which you would
like to ask? . . . Thank you. Miss Burrage, you may stand down.
We may want you again later. Please remain in Court . . . Silence.*

*I propose now to adjourn this Court for half an hour. At the
end of that time I shall call Mary Lamort. If she is not then fit
to give further evidence, we shall have, I am afraid, to adjourn
the hearing. It is getting late.*

XV

THE CORONER

. . . I now declare the Court open. The first duty before us is to hear the further evidence of Mary Elizabeth Lamort . . . Call Mary Elizabeth Lamort.

What's that? What's that? Oh, it's Dr Fothergill. Do you wish to make any statement?

I'm afraid I can't properly hear what you are saying.

Silence! I must have silence in this Court-room! I shall have to have the room cleared if I am annoyed further in this way.

Now then, Dr Fothergill, if you would come up to the table . . . Thank you.

XVI

William Eustace Fothergill, M.R.C.S., L.R.C.P.

Now then, Doctor, what is it that you wish to tell the Court?

I wish to state that in my opinion Miss Lamort should not give evidence today.

And your grounds, Doctor, I suppose are? . . .

Surely they are obvious, Mr Coroner. This is the second time I have been before you during these proceedings. In my confirmed opinion Miss Lamort is in no state to undergo the strain which giving evidence is bound to entail.

I see. Where is Miss Lamort?

Miss Lamort, Mr Coroner, is here. I should add that I am making this protest purely as a medical man because my patient insists that she shall give evidence.

Really? In that case, Doctor, I fail to see why—

It does not interest me, sir, what you see or what you fail to see. I have registered my complete disapproval and I now wash my hands of the whole matter!

I see. In that case, Doctor, may I suggest that you stand down so that we may proceed with the examination of Miss Lamort? This interruption seems to have served no purpose except to waste the time of the Court.

Really, Mr Coroner, I—

I must ask you to stand down, Doctor Fothergill . . . Call Mary Elizabeth Lamort.

XVII

Mary Elizabeth Lamort (recalled)

I understand, Miss Lamort, that it is at your own wish that you are giving evidence again?

Yes.

You wish to make a statement?

Yes.

Is this statement in reference to the evidence given by Violet Burrage?

Yes.

Were you in Court during that evidence? Or did you hear of it?

I was in Court.

I now have to consider whether I will take this additional evidence of yours now or later. I must say that, at the moment, I am inclined—

Oh, please—*please!* I must talk. If I am left on the rack . . . any longer I may . . . I may—

Will you please make your statement.

Yes . . . If I could . . . if I might . . . just . . . I won't keep you a moment . . . I don't know . . . where . . . to begin . . . I am sorry.

Come, Miss Lamort, we are waiting!

Yes. Yes. I know—I—I—I—oh, my God! I must say it, I must! . . . What I said before—was untrue—nearly all of it. Now—I am going to speak the truth, so help me God!

I was Maxwell Brunton's—mistress . . . I—our intimacy— began a fortnight before his death . . . On the Thursday night—he—he—oh, my God!

.   .   .   .

121

Can you resume, Miss Lamort?

Yes. Yes. On Thursday night—on Thursday afternoon, rather—we saw each other for—a little while—less than five minutes. We arranged that I should—if it seemed safe—go into his study after—the others—had gone to bed. We had done it before . . .

I went up to bed at half-past eleven—when—I think it was about three-quarters of an hour later—when I felt certain that the house—that it was safe . . . I—went along to the study—I did not knock—I turned the handle—very quietly—and I went in . . . I must have been so quiet turning the handle—it took me a long time—I did not want to make any sound with the lock—that I must have startled Maxwell . . . Before I could see round the door, I heard him jump up . . . I think he must have knocked his chair over, but he came to meet me . . . He seemed— almost *angry* that I was there. He said it wasn't safe—I had come too early . . . We talked very, very low . . . I went. I crept back to my room, and I went to bed . . . I was angry—angry with Maxwell.

I stayed in bed trying to sleep . . . I did not want to go to him—after that . . . At least, I thought that. But I could not sleep . . . And then I realised that I—had been foolish. I found that I wanted to go back . . . I tried to fight against this—but I could not . . .

I went back—I don't know what the time was. That must have been when that girl saw me. I opened the door in the same way—quietly—very quietly . . . I did not want Maxwell to be angry again . . . And then . . .

  .   .   .   .   .   .

Yes. Yes. Give me a moment. I must say this . . . I mustn't think . . . I mustn't think . . . I mustn't think! I must say this . . . I must make myself—machine—say this . . .

I went in. The light was still on . . . Maxwell lay on the floor . . . There was a place in his head—that should have been . . . There was blood . . . He was dead . . . I did not do anything.

I knew that he—was—dead . . . As I turned to go my foot
brushed against something—and I looked down and saw—the
thing—that he had used as a paper-weight. One end of it was
covered with blood . . . I was—it was as if I was in a nightmare.
But I thought . . . I could do nothing. I could not bring him
back to life. I knew what I must do—for my own sake—for
Enid's sake—for everyone's sake . . . I must go back—back to
my own room and pretend—and swear—and lie—and say that
I had never left it . . .

I went back to—my—own—room—
Quick, man! Catch her! Where's Dr Fothergill?

.   .   .   .   .   .

*Now to resume. I should have liked to have completed the re-
examination of the last witness, but, as you see, her state of health
makes this impossible. She is being attended to by her medical
attendant and I can only hope that she will be well enough to
give further evidence tomorrow if we should require it. In these
circumstances I declare the Court adjourned. It will open
tomorrow at 10.30 a.m. promptly.*

PART THREE

VERBATIM REPORT OF CORONER'S INQUEST (2ND DAY)

The Coroner and Bransby Farquharson, K.C.

I declare the Court open.

Before I commence any other business, I have a communication here which I have received from Mr Bransby Farquharson . . . Is Mr Farquharson in Court?

I am.

Ah, Mr Farquharson, I should have noticed you. Would you be so good as to step up to the table?

Certainly.

Mr Farquharson, you say in your letter that you are watching these proceedings on behalf of Miss Mary Elizabeth Lamort. You also state that, on her behalf, you would like to suggest the recalling of Doctor Crosby and the calling of Sir Philip Fennimore?

That is correct.

Your letter, Mr Farquharson, does not give me any indication of why you wish this further evidence. I presume, of course, that it is on account of the trend of yesterday's evidence which, in regard to Miss Lamort, was of a startling character.

That is correct.

The request, Mr Farquharson, is a somewhat unusual one, as doubtless so eminent a legal luminary as yourself will allow. In fact, I may say that if the request had not come from so distinguished a person as yourself I should have felt inclined to inquire into matters a good deal more closely than I have any intention of doing at the moment. What I would like you to do, though, if you have no objection, is to give the jury your reasons, which you were doubtless too hurried to put in your letter, for wishing to recall Dr Crosby.

Certainly. On behalf of my client I consider it absolutely

essential that the imputations conveyed by the evidence given yesterday by Violet Burrage should be refuted—and refuted immediately. As my client, with truly magnificent courage, stated during her second terrible ordeal in yesterday's proceedings, she does not deny—and what is far more, gentlemen, has no *wish* to deny—that she did, in fact, visit the study of the deceased man at the hour stated by Violet Burrage. But, gentlemen, my client *does* deny that she caused the death of Maxwell Brunton. I put it to you, gentlemen, that if there existed even the shadow of a possibility that proof could be brought forward to show that my unfortunate client—a woman, gentlemen, and a beautiful woman who is now upon the terrible rack of public opinion—I put it to you, I say, that if there existed even the ghost of a chance for my client to bring forward evidence to show that not only did she not kill Maxwell Brunton but that she *could* not have killed Maxwell Brunton—I put it to you, gentlemen, she should be allowed to produce any evidence within her power, or the power of her advisors, to bring forward. How much more then is it essential that this fresh evidence should be heard when it is not a 'ghost of a chance' but a 'cast-iron certainty.' I put it to you, Mr Coroner and gentlemen, that as my client's name can be cleared of the terrible stigma of murder—

One moment, please, Mr Farquharson. This Court is, as you know, purely a Court of Inquiry . . .

Quite, quite. I am merely putting the rational, as opposed to the official, point of view. But in whatever words anyone may cloak the fact of Violet Burrage's evidence yesterday, there is only one logical inference to draw from it until such time as evidence can be produced that my client did not, and, moreover, could not, have killed Maxwell Brunton. And I ask, Mr Coroner, that you will exercise your jurisdiction of this Court in such a way as to permit this terribly grave point to be cleared up to the least possible detail.

Are both Doctor Crosby and Sir Philip Fennimore in court?

Yes, Mr Coroner.

Very well, Mr Farquharson, I will recall Dr Crosby. I would like to ask first, however, whether you will wish to put any questions to these witnesses?

That, Mr Coroner, I am perfectly certain will not be necessary, since Dr Crosby and Sir Philip Fennimore are here to tell you one thing and one thing only. And that is that when Dr Crosby examined the body of Maxwell Brunton at 3.30 a.m. upon the night of Thursday last, that body was in such a state as to prove conclusively to a medical man that death must have occurred *not less than three* hours earlier. And my client, Mr Coroner and gentlemen, did not go into the study, as Violet Burrage's evidence will show and as my client corroborates, until 1.30—by which time Maxwell Brunton's life must have been extinct for at least an hour.

Recall Dr Richard Crosby.

Dr Richard Crosby (recalled)

Dr Crosby, I expect you are aware of the point we have recalled you upon?

Yes.

I will come straight to the point then. Looking up my notes I find that when I asked you, on the occasion of your first giving evidence, how long life had been extinct when you examined the body of the deceased, you said that it had taken place not more than six hours previously. I assume that you now have something to add to this statement?

I have. First I have an apology to make to the Court, and, I have no doubt, to Miss—

Please, Dr Crosby, confine your statement to—

I beg your pardon. When I examined the body of Maxwell Brunton, it was definitely clear that—although it is impossible to fix the *exact* time of death in such a case—death must have transpired *at least* three hours earlier. As I examined the body at 3.30 a.m. this places the latest possible time of death at 12.30 a.m.

I see. You are certain of this, Dr Crosby?

Absolutely and entirely certain! If I were to explain—

One moment, Dr Crosby. If, as I expect, the explanation is a long and technical one, and we are also going to hear the evidence of so renowned an expert as Sir Philip Fennimore, I think we can dispense with your professional reasons for arriving at your decision . . . Do you agree with me, gentlemen? . . . Thank you.

Very well, Dr Crosby, thank you very much. You may stand down.

Call Sir Philip Fennimore.

Sir Philip Fennimore, M.D., B.M., D.Sc., etc., etc.

What is your full name?

Philip August Fennimore.

Will you please take the oath, Sir Philip?

I swear by Almighty God that what I shall say in evidence in this Court shall be the truth, the whole truth and nothing but the truth.

You were in Court, Sir Philip, during the evidence given just now by Dr Crosby?

Yes. I heard Dr Crosby's evidence.

Do I understand, Sir Philip, that Dr Crosby has consulted you upon this matter?

Yes.

And that Dr Crosby provided you with the necessary . . . ah, how shall I put it? . . . data, etcetera, upon which to base an opinion as to when the death of Maxwell Brunton must have occurred?

Yes.

*And you are prepared to corroborate Dr Crosby's dictum?—
that the death must have occurred at 12.30 a.m. at the latest?*

Definitely. There can be no doubt whatsoever that Dr Crosby
is right. It is really a simple point, although perhaps it might
be difficult to explain it to laymen. I have, however, at the request
of Mr Farquharson, prepared a short written statement which
Mr Farquharson can hand to you for the use of yourself and
the jury should you wish to study it.

*Thank you very much, Sir Philip. I don't think we need trouble
you further.*

THE CORONER AND THE JURY

I hope, gentlemen, that you have all taken careful note of the
bearing of the evidence of the last witness.

We have now concluded the primary examination of all
the witnesses, and have recalled one or two. I now propose to
recall Sidney Harrison. We have, I fear, to go over our ground
again.

Recall Sidney Harrison.

NOTE ATTACHED TO DOCUMENTS AS SENT BY SIR EGBERT LUCAS TO COLONEL GETHRYN

A. R. G.,—I am not bothering to send you the verbatim report
of the re-examination of the witnesses. The Coroner is sound
enough but a prolix old fuss-head. There is, you can take it
from me, absolutely nothing new in any of the rest of the
proceedings. I have been over it; Charters has been over it; Pike
has been over it; Jordan has been over it. So, not wishing to
frighten you too much with bulk, I have taken it all out, leaving
the summing up.

The Coroner

It is a curious coincidence, gentlemen, that this morning is the sixteenth anniversary of my introduction to the duty which I am now performing. Sixteen years is a long time. Even the coroner of a quiet rural district will find that in sixteen years he has had many, many inquests over which to preside. How much more, then, if for sixteen years one has been a coroner to a large and very densely populated area of London?

In these sixteen years, gentlemen, I have presided over a very large number of inquests indeed, so large a number that if I were to tell you the total you would probably not believe me. In that large total have been many of a most complex and delicate character—many! But never, gentlemen, have I at the end of any other inquest had to confess myself so completely and utterly at sea as I am at the present moment.

We all know—indeed, I expect some of you know only too well—that we have held daily sessions in this one Court for not less than ten days. During these ten days we have minutely sifted—by means of the examination and re-examination of witnesses, some of whom we have had in the witness chair half a dozen or more times—all the circumstances, however trivial, surrounding the reason for inquest: the death of Maxwell Brunton.

I am sure that you will all agree—I say with the fullest confidence that nobody on earth could fail to agree—that we have left no stone, however small, unturned in our efforts to arrive at the truth of this tangled and vital and, I fear, in some of its aspects, sordid matter. For days we have striven. And yet what have we to show for that striving? What? . . .

I never thought, even up to a time as recent as two days ago, to get such an answer to this question, but now I must say that that answer is: 'We have *nothing* to show.'

You may not, of course, agree with me, gentlemen, but if you do not agree I shall be very, very much surprised. It seems to me that you and I are like men who have been wandering about a maze; not idly wandering, but wandering willynilly; wandering because, although we have been trying with all our might to reach the centre of the maze, we have never succeeded in finding its key and thereby been able to reach the centre.

It is not often that I preface my summing up with such vague generalities. But in this case I cannot help myself. I find that we are no farther, really, than we were at the beginning of the second day of this Court, when we had for the first time taken evidence of all those persons who were under the roof of 44 Rajah Gardens on the night of the death of Maxwell Brunton.

Although it is my personal opinion that each one of you is as fully posted in the evidential details of this extraordinary affair as I am myself, I nevertheless have my duty to do. I have to address you with the equivalent of a judge's summing up. I have to lay before you in brief the whole of the matters which have been engaging our attention in these fruitless days of labour. I am going to be Horatian, gentlemen; I am going to plunge *in medias res*. I am going to start somewhere near the middle and then go back to the beginning again. I am going to say to you, as the first point in this necessary but I fear quite useless speech, that I want you first to consider the relation to this crime of Mary Elizabeth Lamort. After the first evidence of the girl Violet Burrage it appeared to me, as it must have appeared to all of you, that at last we had, so to speak, something which we could catch hold of. We had, after much groping in the dark, a definite piece of circumstantial evidence: Miss Lamort, it appeared, had lied in telling us what she did tell us. Miss Lamort, it appeared, had entered the study at approximately one-thirty a.m. For the first time we had evidence of someone entering that room where Maxwell Brunton was afterward found dead at a time after his withdrawal to it at a few minutes after 11 p.m. But we were doomed to find another blind alley when the police surgeon, Dr Crosby, *and* Sir Philip Tennimore, the great expert, sat in that witness chair and told us, from their specialised knowledge, that Maxwell Brunton must have met his death at a time at least an hour earlier than one-thirty a.m. It then became evident that, however much she may have prejudiced you against her, Mary Lamort was no more to be suspected than other members of the household. Although she may have entered the study at one-thirty a.m., Maxwell Brunton had met his death at some time prior to that. Therefore she could not have killed him; and it seems to me most highly improbable that, if she had killed him at such an earlier time that night as her previous visit—at a time within the possibilities set for us by the men of science—she would have thus revisited the scene of her crime. But, whether you regard that as improbable or the reverse, makes really no matter. Probable or improbable, there is nothing for us, now that she has been acquitted of the possibility of having caused Maxwell Brunton's death at the time she was seen by Violet Burrage entering the study, upon which to base a finding against her. Or if not 'nothing,' at least no more than there is against any other member of the household.

And that last sentence, gentlemen, brings me to what really, I suppose, should be my opening remarks. That is, the prevalence—the extraordinary prevalence—of possible motives for killing the deceased.

It is most highly unusual in my experience—more, it is unprecedented—to find a plethora of motive. Usually, all those concerned with sifting out the truth lying behind a crime of this nature are faced with the one main difficulty of ascertaining motive. In a case where motive is immediately apparent we may be fairly certain that the pinning down of the crime to the actual source is a simple enough matter; and, conversely, in a case where motive is not apparent, we may be absolutely certain that the discovery and eventual punishment of the criminal will be a difficult, tedious, and heartbreaking task.

In other words, gentlemen, *motive* can in nine hundred and ninety-nine cases out of a thousand—or perhaps even a larger percentage than this—be considered the key to the cipher which, translated, is the criminal. And this is where this extraordinary affair first shows its extraordinariness. Instead of having to search for motive, we have motive thrust upon us. If you will go over in your minds the mass of evidence that we have heard in this Court throughout these last ten days, you will find that with the exception of Sydney Harrison, the dead man's secretary; Claire Bayford, the dead man's daughter; and Violet Burrage, the kitchenmaid, every other soul of the house's inhabitants—six in all—had a motive, and a powerful motive, for killing this man.

We are left, then, with six persons: Enid Brunton, the dead man's wife; Adrian, his son; Peter Hargreaves, his guest; Jeannette Bokay, his wife's servant; and Arthur Jennings and his wife, the nucleus of the household staff.

These six persons have each an ostensible motive for killing the man who was killed. Examine them and the motives of which I spoke.

Take, first, Enid Brunton. She has, we know, adored this man; she is his wife; she is, for year upon year, persistently harrowed by the knowledge of his intimacy with other women— and other women drawn from every class of life. Her motive would be primarily jealousy—an emotion all the more intense through having been successfully—how shall I put it?—'bottled up' for so long. Secondarily, her motive would be—though this is not so near the surface as the first—fear for the future livelihood, comfort, and environment of her children and herself.

Next we come to Adrian Brunton, the son. His apparent motive is a threefold one. It is love—because he wishes to marry a certain woman of whom his father cannot or will not approve. It is anger—furious anger—because of this disapproval, and it is an intense desire for money—which he knows he will get in abundance on the death of his father—in order that he may get married.

Next is Peter Hargreaves, the guest. Until after the evidence of the young woman Bokay it seemed that Hargreaves could have no reason for wishing Maxwell Brunton's death; after Bokay's evidence, however, a reason became abundantly obvious. Mr Hargreaves, sitting in that chair, has told you not once but many times that he was completely unaware that his mother had even so much as known Maxwell Brunton, much less that her death might be considered as due to Maxwell Brunton. We have no evidence upon this point.

Next we have the young woman, Jeannette Bokay. She is a Latin; she is, I should say, considerably oversexed, and she is a *discarded* mistress of Maxwell Brunton. In that word 'discarded' lies the possible motive in this instance. I will not insult you, gentlemen, by pointing out that the *crime passionel* is a constant occurrence among all the Latin races. I will merely remind you of this fact and all its implications in this instance. That will give us motive and to spare in the case of Jeannette Bokay.

Next, we have two persons who must count, for reasons of motive at least, as one, Arthur Jennings and his wife Sarah. Here we have motive, and a much more easily comprehensible—though I do not mean to say more powerful—motive than in any of the other instances. Jennings is an escaped convict. Whatever his previous reputation and record may have been, he seems to have been a good and faithful servant to Maxwell Brunton until just before Brunton's death, when the old Adam stirred in him. His theft—a petty one, it is true, but a theft nevertheless—is made known to Maxwell Brunton, but he already knows Jennings's past history. Suppose that Brunton, some days after that interview following the theft of which we have heard almost innumerable times from Jennings and his wife; suppose that he, instead of saying no word regarding his judgment, as the Jenningses have told us, actually stated that in view of Jennings's record he must, for the sake of himself and his household, at once inform the police. What then? Jennings, a man escaped from prison; Jennings, knowing the extra sentence which awaits an escaped convict; Jennings has, has he not? plenteous reason for wishing Brunton's mouth closed in the only permanent way in which a mouth can be closed. But here again we have not one tittle of evidence. We have only what Bokay and the Jenningses have told us, and we have therefore no option but to accept the Jenningses' version of what Brunton said. And if we accept this version—which it is impossible for men to disprove—we destroy practically the Jenningses' motive.

I have now given a survey of the entire household, and in that survey have shown that, out of the total of ten other souls resident in that Rajah Gardens house at the time of Brunton's death, three—Sydney Harrison, Claire Bayford, and Violet Burrage—have no apparent motive whatsoever for causing the death of Maxwell Brunton.

In the second place, I have shown you that Enid Brunton, Adrian Brunton, Peter Hargreaves, Jeannette Bokay, and Arthur Jennings and his wife *have* easily discernible motive for causing the death of Maxwell Brunton.

In the third place— Yes, sir? If you will let me go on, I think you will find that I am about to deal with the point which I imagine you are thinking of raising. In the third place, we have a person resident in the house to whom I have so far made no reference in this part of my speech. I mean, of course, Mary Elizabeth Lamort.

I do not include Mary Lamort in my list of persons without a motive, and I do not include Mary Lamort in my list of persons with a motive. The reason for my omission, I am afraid, may sound paradoxical, but I cannot help that. I do not include Mary Lamort in either of these lists because, in my opinion, gentlemen, Mary Lamort must go down in *both* these lists. As

I have already explained, she is—in spite of evidence which at first seemed black against her—now, by reason of the expert medical testimony in her favour, reduced primarily to an equal level with the other persons in the household. I say that Mary Lamort must go both upon our 'motive' list *and* our 'non-motive' list. She was Brunton's mistress by her own admission. She went to visit Brunton on the night of his death, and by her method of approach to him and her demeanour and apparel equally possibly to enjoy illicit and amorous relations with him, or to quarrel with him. We are not clairvoyant; we cannot see into people's minds. A neurotic woman entangled in a liaison with the husband of her friend might have a thousand motives for killing or none whatsoever. We cannot tell. She must, therefore, be both, so to speak, one of our 'probables' and one of our 'non-starters.'

Now, gentlemen, I am going to leave the first list as it stands: that of the persons with no apparent motive whatsoever for either wishing or causing the death of Maxwell Brunton. But I am going to take that second list, those with a motive, and subdivide it into those with a strong motive and those with a weak motive. Let us examine that list before we split it.

We have Enid Brunton, Adrian Brunton, Peter Hargreaves, Jeannette Bokay, the Jenningses, and Mary Lamort. Consider that list in your minds for a moment, gentlemen, and you will find that the subdivision is easy. In the 'strong-motive' half we shall have Enid Brunton, Adrian Brunton, Jeannette Bokay, and Mary Lamort. In the 'weak-motive' half we shall have Peter Hargreaves, Arthur Jennings, Sarah Jennings, and Mary Lamort . . .

I hope you are following me, gentlemen. I am carrying out, as best I know how, a very difficult task. You will notice that once again one name appears on two lists: that of Mary Lamort. I do not want to seem unduly cryptic. Perhaps I have not been, but Mary Lamort must come up on every one of our lists. She was associated illicitly with the dead man. She did go to see

him in secret that night . . . and yet we know nothing! She must
appear in all classes, so that whatever class we happen to be
thinking about at the moment her name will be there before us
for consideration. We are left, then, like this: I will state this as
a table. It is in my mind as a table.

No Motive.—Sydney Harrison, Claire Bayford, Violet
   Burrage, *and* Mary Lamort.
Weak Motive.—Peter Hargreaves, Arthur Jennings, Sarah
   Jennings, *and* Mary Lamort.
Strong Motive.—Enid Brunton, Adrian Brunton, Jeannette
   Bokay, *and* Mary Lamort.

which, gentlemen, is, I hope, clear, but I am sure, unfortunately,
gets us precisely nowhere!

That table and all that I said before I think may fairly be
held to have codified all the abstract evidence which has been
elicited during these long days upon which the Court has sat.
And yet, I repeat, we are nowhere! We have, it is true, one
common factor—Mary Lamort—but that is all. *Actually* we are
nowhere! Now for concrete evidence:

We have none. Or practically none. We have the fact of
Maxwell Brunton's death, and sworn medical opinion that that
death could not have been self-caused. We have the approximate
time of death; the definite cause of death; and the definite instru-
ment which inflicted that death. And we have, above all, the
practically absolute certainty that the death was caused by an
inmate of the house—by one of those ten people whom, these
past days, we have been questioning and questioning and questioning. We have also one witness who saw one other person in
the house go into the study that night, and secretly. But, as we
have already seen, this piece of evidence, as a help toward arriving
at a really definite conclusion, is valueless. Almost as if it had
never existed. If we had more concrete evidence we might arrive
at a conclusion, but we have not. And, after all our efforts, I am

perfectly certain that we could not get more even if we sat for a year.

It is my considered opinion, gentlemen, that this crime will not—*cannot*—be brought home to any single person unless and until further concrete circumstantial evidence is found. Personally, I do not believe that such further evidence exists. I cannot believe it. You must remember that not only have we been doing our best here in this room, but that, outside, the police, with all their vast resources, all their vast experience, and their terrific energy, have been working to the same end. And they, gentlemen, even with our labours to help them, are not a whit more forward than they were.

It is not out of place for me to say this last, I know, because this morning, before we met here, I discussed the matter with the authorities. They are, I know, going to continue their inquiries. They feel that, however baffled we and they may be at the moment, something, if they continue, may 'turn up.' I must say I doubt it.

Gentlemen, I come to an end feeling more helpless and ineffectual than ever in my life. I can only hope that others, watching my labours, have realised what difficulties—to my mind, insuperable difficulties—have stood and will stand between us and a solution of this affair.

Mr Foreman, I must now formally ask you to consult with the rest of the jury and in due course let me know your verdict. You know, I think, the verdicts which you can return. Do you wish to withdraw and consider your verdict?

Yes, Mr Coroner.

Very well, I will wait.

THE JURY

You have considered, then, and arrived at your verdict?

Yes, Mr Coroner.

It is . . .?

Murder. By person or persons unknown.

Thank you, gentlemen. If I may say so, the only possible verdict in the circumstances.

PART FOUR

LETTER FROM COLONEL ANTHONY GETHRYN TO SIR
EGBERT LUCAS, DATED 6th AUGUST, 193–

My Dear Lucas,

I have had a go at your problem. Although I don't want my penny back, I've rung the bell. But don't take that sentence too blithely. I know who killed this man Brunton. My reasons for being sure you will find later, but you will also find that you are no forrarder. No forrarder, I mean, from your 'give-a-man-a-black-cap-and-hang-him' point of view. You won't be able to do that. I've done this sum, I know, and I'm sending you the answer, but it's not the sort of sum—and the way it's worked out isn't orthodox enough—to produce a verdict of 'Guilty' from any British jury.

When I read your letter I was a good deal annoyed with you, both for trying to spoil my holiday and thinking that you could. And then, when I found that with the suave, bland nerve which I suppose has got you where you are, you had not waited for consent, but had sent me that verbatim report of the inquest proceedings, I became, in these stages, amused at what I thought was your persistence, exasperated by the sight of the unopened bulky folder, curious as to the oddity of an affair which should make you pester me like this, and at last flagrantly avid to try my hand at off-the-spot detection.

It was when I had let this avidity have free play among the shorthand reports that I realised for the first time that it might be possible really to get the answer to the puzzle with nothing else to work on. I then sat down and thought for a week. On the sixth day the thing was in as much of a muddle as ever it had been. On the seventh morning I suddenly saw the key, and within two hours I knew as much as I'm going to tell you. It wasn't until after I'd made the notes of what follows in this letter (that is, it wasn't until after I had worked out my equation), that I wired to you for those photographs of the dramatis personæ. (How the devil, by the way, did you get them all? And how, having got them, were you able to let me have them so quickly?) I merely mention this to show that I was not even helped by knowing what the people looked like. I only wanted to know, as confirmation, what they looked like.

I feel, you know, rather pleased with myself. It was like reading a very good detective story and actually working out before you got to Chapter XXIX—'Crawley Worme Explains'—who *did* kill Lady Hermoine.

But let's get on.

X equals the girl Violet Burrage. There is no doubt of this. You listen, m'sieu, and I show you; yes, like this:

As you know, in any affair at all with which I am concerned from the point of view of 'finding out,' my first rule is to look for oddnesses. It doesn't matter to me whether the oddnesses appear to be related to the crime or not. The fact that odd they are is enough. Sometimes I have to look a long time before I find anything odd. Sometimes I never find anything at all. But this time—well, I ask you! The whole business is an odd business. Right from beginning to end. Instead of having to look for oddities you have them staring goggle-eyed at you from every angle. You have, instead, of the usual search for motive, a perfect gallimaufry of motive handed to you, right at the beginning of the proceedings, on a large salver.

To start: There are, besides the corpse, ten people in the house; and of these ten one or more must have been the slayer. And of these ten, no fewer than *seven* have entirely adequate motives for slaying.

That ought, you know, to be odd enough for one South Kensington murder (incidentally, Lucas, hasn't this opened your eyes about South Kensington? I never thought it of them, I didn't really!) but instead of finishing there the oddities go on. And on. You find, after this orgy of motive, the following:

A very sudden and quite, at first sight, out-of-character cautiousness upon the part of the amorous deceased. You find that the only definite piece of 'accusative' evidence is at the same time at least part of an alibi for the accused. You find that the donor of this accusative evidence has, apparently, the gift of being able to see through solid bodies! And you find, lastly, that this accuser (apart from his, her, or its appearance—which is only corroborative) suffers from an odd affliction.

We will now go back to the beginning again. We will take our first oddness. There is too much motive. Those seven people who have between them this excess of reason for killing have been most exhaustively dealt with by the coroner—he does not, I must say, seem quite such a fool as coroners generally are—and so, therefore, we leave them. But what do we do? We look at those people who have *not* got, apparently, any motive. Don't think I'm mad or drunk. I mean it. This is an odd business and therefore we must get at it in an odd way. In the usual case, where the perpetrator of a crime is hidden, the book of rules says, 'Look for motive.' In this case we must turn the book of rules upside down. Get me? It is odd that there should be a lot of motive, but there *is* a lot of motive. Therefore it is odd, *this* time, that there should be people without motive. I hope you follow, but whether you do or not, you've got to come along.

I said, let's look at the people *without* motive. They are Sydney Harrison (what an unpleasant little creature), Claire Bayford, and Violet Burrage, the kitchenmaid. There they are. Inscribe their names in letters of fire upon your brain and hold them there. We now make a table: a table of the oddities of which I have just spoken. It comes out, slightly rearranged, like this:

Oddity 1.—Three persons, out of ten, *without* motive.
Oddity 2.—Accuser of Mary Lamort—deliverer of Mary Lamort.
Oddity 3.—The accuser of Mary Lamort has X-ray eyes.
Oddity 4.—Maxwell Brunton develops, on *first* visit upon the fatal night of Mistress Mary Lamort, unusual and excessive caution because of . . .?

We will now do that table all over again and put against each oddity the answer or equivalent to that oddity. Thus:

ODDITY	EQUIVALENT
1. 3 persons *without* motive.	Sydney Harrison, Claire Bayford, *Violet Burrage.*
2. Accuser and clearer of Mary Lamort.	*Violet Burrage.*
3. Accuser of Mary Lamort has X-ray eyes.	*Violet Burrage.*
4. Maxwell Brunton develops excessive caution because of	*Violet Burrage.*

Look at this. You may not see just yet why I have put Violet Burrage's name as the equivalent to the last two oddities. You may not even see what I mean by the third oddity. But you will see that, in regard to (1) she is all right; that in regard to (2) she is all right; (it was her evidence that first got Lamort really into trouble, and it was her evidence—by showing that the second visit of Lamort to the study was at one-thirty—that freed Lamort of the possibility of having killed Brunton on that second visit). Now for (3) and (4). I will show you that Violet is also the right answer here. But I must first show you, perhaps what (3) means. In her evidence, Violet exhibits a complete knowledge of the Lamort's attire. Violet knows (1) that the nightdreth wath black; (2) that it wath thilk; (3) that it had jutht a thort of wrap over it; (4) that thith wrap wath jutht a thin thing; (5) that it had bright colourth *on the front*; (6) that Lamort was wearing a great green stone which could not have been worn by anyone else in the house.

Look at your plan; the plan that the coroner had; the plan that you sent me; the plan that everybody has been looking at so long that they've quite forgotten to make any meaning out of it. When she saw Lamort, she (Violet) was coming out of the linen cupboard, and Lamort, Violet says, was coming out of Lamort's room. Look at Lamort's room. There is, we know from Violet, a light on the landing, a light which is apparently sufficient to show up—though it must be fairly dimly—the whole of the corridor down to the study. But Violet says that when she saw Lamort, 'the'd' (Lamort had) 'jutht come out of her room. The wath jutht thutting the door.'

Look again at your plan and you will see which way the doors open. Lamort, to have been shutting her door, is almost certain to have had her back to the landing and the linen cupboard. Lamort was going to the study. Lamort—unless it had been for one brief let's-have-a-look-and-see-if-anyone's-about glance, far too swift to show herself in detail to anyone just peeping—would not at all have faced the landing or the linen cupboard. She was going to the study, and she went (Violet says so) to the study.

Now, even supposing that Lamort was feeling gymnastic and wanted to shut the door behind her back, and did in fact shut the door behind her back, facing while she did so toward the linen cupboard and the landing, is it possible that Violet could have seen in such detail a no doubt very attractive costume? It is not likely; it is so damn unlikely as to be virtually impossible. So much for that third oddity.

Now for the fourth. That oddity was: Maxwell Brunton develops, on the *first* visit of Mistress Mary Lamort to the study, unusual and excessive caution because of Violet Burrage.

This is a difficult one, but it's all right. Look here. First, we may believe the second evidence of Lamort. No one, much less an erotic and neurotic woman of this description, who probably isn't such a bad sort, can lie in layers. Her first lie took it all out of her. Her second statement was the truth. Now, then: Brunton is 'carrying on,' to the limit, with Lamort. Brunton is an entirely experienced lover and manager of women. Brunton has made a date with Lamort. The appointment was for no definite time. Brunton said, in effect, 'Come along when the coast's clear.' Lamort, accordingly, knowing that the house was abed (she had come up with the main body and must have listened and heard Claire Bayford and Hargreaves go to their rooms a bit later), went along to the study at about a quarter-past twelve. But is she welcome? She is not. Maxwell, she tells us, made a bit of a racket as she was mousily entering and before she could see round the door. (She says, 'I heard him jump up. I think he must have knocked his chair over.') Maxwell lets her come in, but only just in. Maxwell is cross. Maxwell says something like, 'No, no, it's not safe! You must go away and come back later!' Ridiculous! If it is not safe, the danger of discovery is doubled by sending the poor lady immediately back over her hazardous journey. But if it *is* safe, why send her back? Obviously, the man is concerned *not* with the *possibility* of someone else (*a*) coming in *or* (*b*) overhearing, but with the *certainty* of someone (*a*) coming in; (*b*) overhearing, or (*c*) *being in already*, and of these three alternatives, I want to make you, Lucas, take the third.

If the certainty had been that someone outside the room was at the time about to come in in a position to overhear, Brunton could have said nothing. There wouldn't have been time. He would either have just whispered, 'Go!' with such intensity that she would have gone, realising the urgency, or he would have taken her in and either faced the music or hidden her. If the certainty had been that someone was at some future time going to come in or to be able to overhear, he would have told her so: what he would have told her would have been that the someone who was going to come in or to be in a position to overhear was his wife. He would have said this whether it was true or not, because this would be a satisfactory explanation to Lamort and also an explanation which would effectively make her realise the necessity for going. But he followed neither of these courses, and, therefore, if you really think about this, you will see that the danger lay not outside that room at all, but inside it. That is, *that there was some other person in that room at that time.*

Who was this? Who could it have been? The only way to find this out is by elimination. It could not have been his wife: she would not have consented to being hidden. It is most highly improbable that it was his daughter, for the same reason. It could not have been any male member of the household, for any one of them would either (1) have objected, at least long enough for the plan to go agley, to being hidden, or (2) and this is the more probable, Brunton would never have allowed Lamort to enter the room. He saw that door opening; he was waiting for Lamort. If he had had a man with him he would have been at that door in a flash. He was, as sticks out very plainly from the evidence, a very decent person of his kind. (Is that good enough for you about the men? I could go on, but unless you send me a special prepaid cablegram I shan't. Think it out.)

That exhausts the non-starters, and we are left with Sarah Jennings, Jeannette Bocquet, and Violet Burrage.

Sarah Jennings I am going to scratch. She could only have had one reason for being in the study at such an extraordinary time, and that would be for the purpose of silencing Brunton in order that he might not send her Arthur back to finish his stretch. The improbability of this is so vast that no backing to it is really required, but just in order to be tidy, I will point out that, if this woman— this cheerful, humorous, fifty-year-old Cockney dame—had so screwed herself up that she was actually contemplating killing 'the Master' (unthinkable thought!) she would have been unable to do it in anything save one violent upheaval. She could not—it is psychologically impossible—have talked to the Master first, and allowed the Master to hide her when the Master's lady came in. She could only have burst in, picked up the rockery, and done the job right away. If, being about to kill him, she had spoken at all, it would have been to 'give him the rough edge of her tongue!' in which case the rough edges would have been heard quite easily by Lamort, and she, Lamort, would never have entered.

You may say that Sarah might have gone to the study to 'plead' with the Master. Not a bit of it. That, too, is psychologically impossible for the woman. Certainly she would have seen the Master at a proper time and have made a great to-do about asking to see him first.

Now we have Number Two. A very different matter. Jeannette Bocquet. A Gallic young woman with apparently some looks and let us say 98 per cent, vigorous S. A. I submit that the person in the study could not have been Bocquet any more than it could have been any of the others. Bocquet had had her flutter with M'sieu. She admitted it. (I expect she was quite proud of it, and I think that, in that respect, her evidence was quite truthful except, of course, for the obvious lie about herself having terminated the intimacy.) You may say that Bocquet may have wanted to renew the fun and games with M'sieu, and that she may, looking deliberately provocative, have gone into the study knowing that the rest of the household was in bed. I say no. At her first entrance, almost before she had got within the door, Brunton would have sent her packing. He was waiting for Lamort; he had, in effect if not in fact, given a promise to his son that the Bocquet matter was closed for ever. I say, too, that Bocquet herself would not have done this. She is, as I see her, an intriguing, treacherous, clever, and passionate little piece. She might, it's true, quite easily—out of the purely animal part of her mind—have conceived the idea of killing the man who had thrown her over. But that would have been much nearer in time to the throwing over. It would have been an act done in white-hot rage, and not even a discarded young Frenchwoman can remain in a white-hot rage for more than a month. It can't be done.

Further, she is a shrewd girl, obviously. She is also by nature a spy. There was very little that went on in that house that she did not know. You saw that. If she did not actually know that Lamort was M'sieu's latest, she must have guessed it. So that, even supposing her to have suddenly wished for a renewal of relations with M'sieu, she would have known that all attempts at this must wait until Lamort had gone. Personally, I don't think she ever wanted to resume relations. She obviously liked her job, or she wouldn't have stayed in it so long—there are plenty of vacancies for good ladies' maids in London—and, liking her job, any attempts to renew relations with M'sieu would be, obviously, a bad step. M'sieu was finished. M'sieu would be angry. Although M'sieu would be unlikely to report directly to Madame, things might nevertheless go awkwardly for Jeannette.

And think of Jeannette—think of Jeannette's evidence—what was it but a display of all-round venom shooting? Do you think if Jeannette *had* been the person in the study that night, had seen Mary Lamort come in, in the manner and clothes in which she did come—do you think that Jeannette could have sat in that witness chair and missed that chance! Impossible!

A field of three, and two scratched. Violet Burrage walks over. It *was* Violet Burrage. And it was because Violet Burrage was hidden in the study when Mary Lamort went there for the first time that Violet Burrage was able to see and so closely notice what Lamort was wearing.

Look at the plan of the study. You will see that the only place in which a human being could be hidden and hidden quickly is the curtained-off alcove of the bay window. (Remember that scuffle—Mary Lamort thought he had knocked over a chair—which Mary Lamort heard while she was opening the door! That was Violet going into hiding.) And from these curtains Violet could look out without being seen; look out and see Mary Lamort and *how she was dressed*, down to the very embroidery upon the front of her wrap and the big emerald pendant hung about her throat.

Proving that Violet is the right and proper equivalent to every one of those oddities of mine seems to have taken rather longer than I thought it would. But you will find that I have done it. What I have to do now is, first, to remind you what these oddities were, like this:

1. Violet Burrage had no apparent motive in a household full of motives.
2. Violet Burrage went out of her way to accuse Mary Lamort and in the same breath acquitted Mary Lamort.
3. Violet Burrage knew down to the smallest detail what

Mary Lamort was wearing and yet could not (if her evidence at the inquest was correct) have seen this.

4. Violet Burrage, hidden in the study, was the cause of Mary Lamort being sent packing upon her first visit.

And then to rewrite and rearrange this table, like this:

1. Violet Burrage was in Maxwell Brunton's study when Mary Lamort first came in. Violet Burrage was, therefore, the cause of Mary Lamort being sent away.

2. Because she was in the study and therefore (peering out from behind the curtains) could see, Violet Burrage knew what Lamort had on.

3. Violet Burrage, trying to incriminate Lamort, overlies and oversteps herself and makes a mistake which leads to Mary Lamort being at least temporarily cleared.

4. Violet Burrage had no apparent motive either for trying to incriminate Lamort or for killing Maxwell Brunton.

Look at that now, and you will see that No. 3, if properly handled, may eliminate No. 4; that is to say, that an analysis of Violet Burrage's incriminatory clearance of Lamort may supply that lacking motive. Like this:

Violet Burrage did not, in fact, see Lamort at all going to or during that *second* visit of Lamort's to the study. Burrage, as I have shown, was in the study during Lamort's *first* visit, and she could not have stayed in the study or near it for more than a few minutes after Lamort's first departure. Brunton (see later) would not have tolerated her presence for a moment longer than was necessary to let Lamort get back to her room. Either, therefore:

1. Brunton rid himself of Burrage's presence,

or

2. Burrage killed Brunton.

In either event, Burrage does not—would not, could not—stay in the room. If Brunton is alive he throws her out, metaphorically or literally; if Brunton is dead, his deadness, and the fact that she is its cause, gets rid of her as quickly. If Brunton is alive, she can stay neither in nor near the study. If Brunton is dead, she can stay neither in nor near the study. Ergo: she was neither in nor near the study during Lamort's *second* visit. Ergo: she is lying when she says she saw Lamort going toward that second visit. Now, why should she trouble to lie—when even to her (see later) distorted and diseased little mind, she must be perfectly safe from having Brunton's death put down to her address? Why should she trouble, I say, to lie, to incriminate another woman when that lying, as well as incriminating the other woman, *may draw attention to herself*; may crack, by making her have to admit that she was *not* inside her room for the whole of the dangerous hours, that hitherto invulnerable shell of 'obviously-nothing-to-do-with-it' armour which has surrounded her? There can be only one answer—jealousy! And jealousy of a morbid and ingrowing kind; suppressed, soul-destroying jealousy which by reason of its suppression fattens on itself.

But what class of jealousy? Merely by reading the evidence, you will find—as I found long before I got the confirmation of that picture gallery you sent me—that Violet Burrage is, to say the least of it, entirely lacking in physical or mental charm; utterly devoid of genuine S. A., utterly devoid, even, of purely surface animal attraction. If she had not been devoid of these things—if she had not been one of those unfortunate creations which, although they are roughly made in the shape of a woman, cannot be considered by the complementary sex as anything more interesting than a clumsy, amateur-built robot—we should have heard of her during the inquest as a *possible* mistress for Brunton.

The coroner, when he found he was going to get no change out of a search for circumstantial evidence, very soundly began '*chercher la femme inconnue.*' To every witness—or nearly every witness—he put the specific question: 'If Maxwell Brunton were conducting an intrigue [*sic*] at the time immediately preceding his death with someone in the household, who would that someone most probably have been?' He got, you will remember, no answer at all from Enid Brunton, Claire Bayford, and Peter Hargreaves; but he did get answers from Adrian Brunton and Jeannette Bocquet. Adrian Brunton, knowing that at one time at least there had been fun and games with Bocquet, gave Bocquet. Bocquet, denying (I am sure, in this instance, truthfully, for reasons which I have given above) that the fun and games had ever been restarted, threw out on general principles a veiled hint of Lamort, for she could not—it was impossible for her to—either leave a question unanswered or avoid innuendo. But—and here's my point at last!—she made no hint or suggestion concerning Violet Burrage. And why? Because, as a woman, Violet Burrage didn't exist. Do you think it at all possible, that if there had been even the remotest likelihood of Brunton even resting a conscious eye momentarily upon Violet, that Bocquet would not have had something to say about Violet? You don't. Of course you don't! Violet was disregarded as a possibility, and quite rightly. It isn't necessary, but if you like to, just have a look at Vi's photograph, or, better still, go and look at Vi herself. No man—certainly no man of Brunton's class and tastes—could possibly have desired her.

So that—(Yes, yes! I quite remember where I am. I am in the process of showing how Violet Burrage's attempt to incriminate Lamort gives us the motive for her killing of Brunton—have patience!) So that this jealousy of Violet's toward Lamort could not have been as from one concubine to another. What, then, was its basis? To get the answer, we must work like this:

1. Violet was in the study on that night and was hidden by, or with the knowledge or consent of, Maxwell Brunton.

But,

2. Violet is completely undesirable, and Maxwell Brunton, knowing that Lamort was coming to the study, could not *in any case* have intended to permit Violet's entry.

But,

3. The probability that it was a sex reason which led to *this* kitchenmaid being alone with *that* master in such a way, is so great as to become a certainty.

Therefore,

4. Since, toward Violet, Maxwell Brunton could have had no inclination whatsoever, the sex-governed impulse which led to Violet being in the study must have been Violet's own.

Therefore again,

5. Violet's jealousy of Lamort was based upon raging envy. Envy of beauty; envy of sex satisfaction; envy of that satisfaction being obtained from Maxwell Brunton.

So much for the reason of Violet's jealousy of Lamort. Now—and this is easy—to get, from this, at Violet's motive for killing Brunton. But we will, for tidiness, go through the 'how' before getting to the basic 'why.'

There can be no question that this killing was absolutely unpremeditated. I don't think that it could be called murder. If it ever became possible—which it never will, my poor policeman!—to bring Violet Burrage to trial for causing the death of Maxwell Brunton, the verdict—if it were not an acquittal—would be manslaughter. You cannot seriously suppose that Maxwell Brunton would sit quite

still, having put himself into a nice easy position, while a
repulsive-looking girl shoved a piece of rock through his
right eye into his brain. If the killer had been a paramour,
or a possible paramour of Brunton's, such a thing might
have been possible. (I mean that, beautifully at ease with
the loved one, Brunton might have laid himself open to
a deliberate blow. He might, for instance, have been sitting
or lying back in a big chair with the woman wandering
about the room, in which case she could have upped
with the quartz and have pushed it through his eye from
behind.) But not so Violet. Impossible for Violet. Brunton
was a big and fit man. Violet is a little and unfit creature.
If she had picked up the quartz and run at him with it,
she would not have got anywhere near her object. Couldn't
have. Similarly, at no time while Violet was in the room
would Brunton have sat down with his back to her. He
would not have sat down, as a matter of fact, at all. He
must have been too astonished. His one idea must have
been to get out of this ludicrous and rather uncomfortable
position as quickly as possible. He would remain standing,
telling the girl not to be crazy, telling her to go. The only
way, therefore, in which Violet could have killed him was
by *throwing*—no doubt at very close range—the lump of
mineral. And what does throwing imply? Sudden, blind
impulse . . . I will tell you how it happened—how it must
have happened—and during this telling the motive will at
least begin to appear.

I will start right at the beginning. Maxwell Brunton,
having in the afternoon made a date with Lamort, goes
down to the drawing-room at about eleven o'clock,
spreading the news that he is to be busy in his study for
some time yet and that therefore he will say good-night
now. He says good-night. He goes back to his study.
Probably the only work he has to do is to keep calm while
he is waiting for his visitor. Presently—at just about the

time, probably, when he is beginning to be unable to sit still any longer—the door begins softly to open. Being neither a young nor an inexperienced lover, he does not run toward it. He stands looking nonchalant; but nevertheless he is quite suitably afire within. The door opens slowly, very slowly. The person who is opening it is trying—and reasonably—not to make any noise. And then, when the door is fully open and the opener is within the room, closing the door, he looks. He looks once. He looks twice. He shuts his eyes and opens them again. No, they are not playing him false . . .

Instead of the regal, entirely sophisticated and enticingly apparelled beauty of Mary Elizabeth Lamort, he sees—crazy though it all must seem—the squat, undersized, certainly hideously clothed (I wonder what she *did* wear, Lucas?) entirely sexless ugliness of his kitchenmaid. I should think he has to look three or four times before he even remembers her face. He says at last: ' What in the name of everything do *you* want?' But he doesn't shout. Even in his astonishment he is careful. He knows too well his own reputation. He knows too well what to expect if this extraordinary visitation is ever discovered. Who will believe—who—that he had nothing to do with it? It would be useless for him just to point to the girl and say, 'Well, I ask you!' Quite useless. It might work in another man's case, but not in his. In his it would probably merely be set down to a diseased dimming of his appreciations . . . No! he must get rid of her swiftly; he must get rid of her quietly.

He waits for some explanation, and while he waits he thinks furiously. Not only has he got to get rid of her and get rid of her quietly, but also he has got to get rid of her before Mary comes, because Mary, too, knows his reputation. Mary *might* not believe, and Mary—even if she did believe, and, believing, were not disgusted—what would Mary feel if her visit (and did he not well know how she would be attired for that visit?) were known by this—this dreary little goblin, who must certainly be mad? . . . What can the goblin want? She seems to be trying to tell him . . .

A most painful business, Lucas, and not a very nice one. We will draw veils until the moment when Maxwell Brunton realises, with utter amazement, the reason for the girl's presence. Because he is an extremely kindly man and an imaginative one, and also because of this necessity for silent speed, he is pleasant to her. Perhaps even fatherly. A sort of 'There-there-you-run-away-and-don't-be-a-silly-little-girl-but-for-Heaven's-sake-run-away-without-making-any-noise' sort of attitude. But it doesn't work. It inflames the unfortunate creature. She, too, is making no noise, no unnecessary sound at all. She, too, wishes no interruption—but for a different reason. She is talking, talking; even perhaps trying to act . . . And then poor Brunton hears a sound—the noise of his door handle again. There is nothing for it. He thinks like lightning, picks the girl up bodily, takes three steps, and is at the curtained-off alcove of the bay window. He rams her behind the curtains and leaves her there and trusts to God that she will have the sense from every point of view to keep quiet. (The noise of the action is the sound which made Mary think he had 'jumped up in a hurry.')

He crosses the room to Mary. He is in a situation to tax even his ingenuity. He wants to explain to Mary, nicely so that she will not be offended, that it is not yet safe. He thinks of so many stories all at the same time that not one of them will come out. He succeeds in getting rid of Mary, but he also succeeds—and miserably knows it—in both hurting and angering her . . .

So soon as the door shuts—softly, softly—behind her, he stands by his table. He says, bitterly, but still in that low voice: 'Better come out now!' He is at the side of the writing table away from the window and at the corner of the writing-table nearest the fireplace. There is a moment before his order is obeyed, and during that moment he sees that the curtains are just parted as if someone were holding them and looking through. He realises that they have probably been thus held, that an eye has been to the aperture, all the time. That makes him angry. He repeats the order more harshly. This time there is an answer to it. The curtains part, and out comes the tragic grotesqueness. And now! Now, she is no longer inflamed by the one devouring urge. Now she has, added to this insanity, the madness of wild, mind-storming envy. She has been looking at the lovely demi-goddess who has, and is to have, all that she herself wants—or thinks she wants—out of this terrible business of living. She went behind those curtains as a distraught, shivering girl. She comes out from behind those curtains as a berserk woman. Brunton is standing, as I told you. She walks straight forward. All she can see is the face of this man. It dances like a devil-Tantalus before those staring eyes of hers. She comes up against the table with a little shock. She finds that she cannot walk farther; there is something in the way. Still she stares at that face. Against her hand she finds that there is something cold and hard. She closes her fingers over it. It is heavy. Still she stares at that face . . . She lifts her right hand and arm. In the hand is the thing she had caught hold of. She draws back her arm. Suddenly, with a force and truth possible to her only by the supernormal state she is in, she flings the thing, with all her might, at the face . . .

It may have been a minute; it may have been half an hour before enough of what we may call sanity returns to her and she sees what she has done. She may have knelt by the body; she may not. I think not. I think that, realising dully—her mind is just a painful numbness—she goes away from that room. Probably she makes no effort at silence and therefore, as is the way, is at least so silent that no one hears her. Certainly no one sees her. She goes straight from that place and straight back to her own little place . . .

And then, when Harrison and the policeman come to wake her, she is in a state which is not so much sleep as a stupor of the mind . . .

And because she has the protection of this mental state, her speech and actions seem in no way unusual—in no way unusual, that is, in an utterly unimportant servant girl whose doubtless small mind is only able to compass the thought that 'something awful has happened—the master's dead!' She may seem dazed—quite natural! She may seem so frightened as to be stupid and to be unable at first to answer questions properly—quite natural! All quite natural.

And then the days between death and the beginning of the coroner's inquest. During those days some of the numbness wears off. Now she can once more order her own thinking, and, ordering her own thinking, she comes to a return not, indeed, of that awful hunger for the man who is dead—that, although she does not know it, could easily be transferred to practically any male human—but to a return of the searing envy of that other woman who has, although after all she is only a woman, everything that a poor girl lacks. This envy becomes, growing hour by hour, day by day, night by night, an obsession even greater than had the other obsession been. It grows until it turns into a wish; and the wish is for the extermination of this other woman, this lucky woman, this woman who has everything. And then comes the realisation that maybe there is a means by which this other may be not only exterminated but made to suffer in the course of her extermination.

Here, the thought runs, if someone were to tell that Mary Lamort had been in the study that night? No one except Violet knows yet. But why should they not know it? Why should not Violet say? That's the beginning. From there the steps are easy and quick. But still the obsession clouds the thought processes and spoils them. Spoils them so that in the end their expression cancels itself out. These thought processes went, I think, something like this:

Must tell them about her. But be careful! Don't tell them about her at the time when she was there; because if at that time anyone happened to know that you were out of your room, then danger for you! Tell them about her at another *time; make it up! Say that you* did *leave your room at this made-up time and that you saw her go into the study. It won't matter what she says; she knows she's been to the study. She knows she hasn't told anyone. She'll behave so that it'll come out and they'll think that she did it. And I believe she* did *see him after! I believe she did go back the way he asked her to. So, if you tell properly about that made-up time . . . Anyhow, it'll make them* think *she did it! . . .*

Something like that, the thoughts went, but the poor, muddled, sick little mind couldn't be bothered with details like time of death and how long the body had been dead when it was found. It couldn't cope with that sort of thing, and that is why there was that super-oddity—the oddity, Lucas, which was really my starting point in this thing— of Mary Lamort's accuser being at the same time Mary Lamort's deliverer. If, for her lie, Violet Burrage had chosen a time which would have fitted in with the doctors', then Mary Lamort would have been in grave danger. Luckily for Mary Lamort, the little mind could not be bothered . . .

There you are, sir. That's my reconstruction. I'm not—

however much I may appear to the contrary—unduly conceited, but I would bet half my income to a tin of bull's-eyes that that reconstruction, if wrong at all, is wrong only in detail. In essence it is right—must be right!

But I can hear you beginning to moan. You are wanting, now that you have had the 'how,' the full, real 'why.' A good deal of it, of course, if not all of it, appears in my description of the 'how,' but to tidy this long, but I hope not too rambling, statement up properly, I will set out the motive for you. Briefly, like this:

Violet Burrage is one of those unhappy young women with an abnormally unpleasing exterior, an abnormally uninteresting personality, a subnormal education so rudimentary that her mind can find no solace for her bodily troubles, and an abnormal sex impulse. She is, in short and in the vulgar tongue, a woman whose very existence is repulsive to men and a woman whose very existence is centred on the desire to be attractive to men. What her mental condition was before she took service in Brunton's house it is impossible to say, but I should think that already, young girl though she was, her mind was beginning to become obsessed with the sex idea, probably owing to her complete failure to achieve even the occasional society of any male.

The effect of the atmosphere of the Brunton household can have done nothing but exacerbate this condition. (If it did not exacerbate it, it started it and made it grow, but I think exacerbate is right.) She does not, in her position, of course, see much of the Family or the Master, but she hears things. She cannot help hearing things. She is in touch with Bocquet, for one thing, and although Bocquet may not have anything to do with her, she has to do with the Jenningses, and Bocquet talks to the Jenningses. And to what Bocquet says to the Jenningses and what the Jenningses say to Bocquet, Violet listens.

Soon the atmosphere of 'easy love' begins to seep into her mind . . .

And that mind is already distorted . . .

From this point to that scene which I have tried to reconstruct for you above is one step and, if you think about it, a very short step. The whole tragic, unhappy business is only difficult to understand, is only hard to believe, if one does not think. If one thinks, it is easy. An obsession can make madmen of us all. An obsession made a madwoman of Violet Burrage. It was her obsession which took her on that preposterous visit. It was her obsession which threw the weapon that killed Brunton.

I don't think there's anything else for me to say. As I pointed out at the beginning—and as you must by this time agree—there is no chance of bringing Violet Burrage to trial on this statement of mine. I know she did it. You, I think, after reading this, will also believe she did it. But we both know that good old roast-beef, brussels-sprouts English law will not listen to such stuff. It would merely murmur the word 'psychology' and shy across the road. In only one way is it a pity that Violet Burrage cannot be tried, and that is, that that seems the only way to have her treated at a stage when a cure is possible. She could not be hanged. She could not be given penal servitude. All that could happen would be mental treatment, and that might save her from ultimate actual lunacy.

Yours ever,
A. R. GETHRYN

APPENDIX

I

Letter and Enclosure dated 20th August, 193– from Sir Egbert Lucas to Colonel Anthony Ruthven Gethryn

Scotland Yard,
20th August, 193–

My Dear Gethryn,

First of all, officially, I have to convey the thanks, appreciation and admiration of the Commissioner for the really brilliant bit of work contained in the letter you sent us dated 6th August. Secondly and unofficially, I have to pat you on the back myself. You will never do anything better—largely because, or so it seems to me, that that would be impossible.

I read your document first, not once but three times. Then I took it to Charters, and, for the whole of the day following, we argued. He went away apparently convinced that your reasoning was too clever to be solid, but, by the following day, he had turned right round and was as convinced that you were right about the girl Burrage being the author of Brunton's death as you appear to be.

We took the document round to the D.P.P. We left it there—and that, I'm afraid, is that. No, we couldn't move Marshall an inch. He, too, was quite convinced that you were right, but he was equally convinced that, as you said, it would be a hopeless task to try and convict on the evidence. The reason Charters and I are so sick about the business is that we feel, not so much that the wretched Burrage needs any more punishment than she is likely to have in her own mind, but that it seems so damned hard on the decent members of the Brunton household. I am afraid it is inevitable that they will go through at least the next ten years of their lives with a great many people looking askance at them as possible murderers. *C'est la vie!* We can't do anything to avoid this or you can take it that we would.

Once more with my very heartiest congratulations and thanks and with very best wishes to your wife and son.

Yours very sincerely,
E. Lucas

P.S.—Pike sends his respects. He is very downcast. He has read your opus and the incredible has happened—his veneration of you has actually increased, a thing I had thought impossible! He is walking about with a face as long as a mule! The trouble is, from his point of view, that here is your best case and it is never going to be acknowledged. I pointed out to him that this would probably actually please you, but he is still inconsolable.

II

LETTER, DATED 21ST DECEMBER, 193-, from SIR EGBERT
LUCAS TO COLONEL ANTHONY GETHRYN

SCOTLAND YARD,
21st December, 193-

MY DEAR GETHRYN,

You remember *l'affaire* Brunton? Well, an end has
come to it after all. And it is an end which you ought to
be extraordinarily pleased about. Before it came, however
much we may have said, we agreed with you, you had no
real proof that you were right. Now, as you will see from
the enclosed cutting from last night's *Planet*, you have.

At eleven o'clock yesterday morning the Inspector in
charge of the Blackfriars Road Station was told that a
young woman wanted to see him. She refused to state her
business to the sergeant at the desk, but insisted on seeing
the Inspector. Not being busy, he had her in. Never having
had anything to do with the Brunton business, he did not
recognise her. He asked her for her name, which she
refused to give. What she did give him, however, was a
very full foolscap envelope. It was addressed to 'The Head
of the Police.' The girl, of course, was Burrage. The
Inspector got nothing out of her. She steadfastly refused
her name, and, equally steadfastly, refused to say what this
envelope was that was to go to the 'Head of the Police.'
In his report he states that: 'in my opinion, the young
woman was mentally afflicted.' He was doubtless right.
He eventually humoured her and accepted the envelope,
having, of course, when he accepted it, no more intention
of forwarding it here than of sending it to the man in the

moon. Unfortunately—or should I say fortunately?—he put the envelope on one side and forgot about it for nearly twenty-four hours. When he read it he altered his mind very quickly. In fact he was round here, so they tell me, in something under the previous record time! I cannot, I'm afraid, send you a copy of this amazing thing just yet. I have read it myself, but as yet am not able to send it to you. I will do so as soon as I possibly can. I am sending this letter by air mail. You may, of course, have seen the papers before you get it, but, knowing your habits, I think this is unlikely.

Yours in haste,
E. G. L.

CUTTING FROM THE *Evening Planet*.
ISSUE DATED DECEMBER 20, 193–

BRUNTON MURDER REVELATION

SERVANT GIRL'S SUICIDE

FULL CONFESSION

How she killed Maxwell Brunton, and why, was the subject of an astonishing human document received this morning by the police from Violet Ethel Burrage, whose dead body was found in the Thames at Blackwall last night.

Thought it would drive her mad

In the confession—which, the *Planet* is able to state, is fully accepted by the police—Burrage states that, although she knew she was safe from detection, her conscience was too strong for her. She says, 'I can't stand it any longer. I think I'm going mad.'

Astounding Revelations

A representative of the *Planet* called this afternoon on Dr Howard Ellington, the famous alienist. Dr Ellington admitted that Burrage's confession had been forwarded to him by the authorities at Scotland Yard.

'I'm afraid,' Dr Ellington explained, 'that I am naturally not in a position to divulge the specific contents of this extraordinary document. Nor,' he added, 'can I. I am afraid, discuss it, beyond stating that it is one of the most poignant revelations of the turmoil which may ravage the human soul that it has ever been my lot to see.

'This poor girl was not a criminal.' Dr Ellington paused here and added: 'Perhaps when our civilisation becomes more enlightened than it is today such tragedies will be averted. Much could be done for the Violet Burrages of this world if our educational system were not the futile and puerile thing that it is.'

Baffled Scotland Yard.

So ends one of the most extraordinary murder cases of the past decade. For weeks and weeks before, during, and after the fruitless coroner's inquest the police worked day and night to elucidate the mystery. They were, in fact, still engaged upon the apparently hopeless task when, like a bolt from the blue, the extraordinary confession burst upon them.

LETTER AND ENCLOSURE DATED 12TH JANUARY, 193– FROM SIR EGBERT LUCAS TO COLONEL ANTHONY RUTHVEN GETHRYN

SCOTLAND YARD,
12th January, 193–

MY DEAR GETHRYN,

Many thanks for your letter of last Monday. I am glad to hear that you and your family are in such fettle, but equally depressed to hear that it will be another four months or so before you will be back in London again.

I am afraid it is not a bit of good reviling me on account of your name having got into the papers in regard to the solving of the Brunton case: I am not guilty. Neither is Charters. So far as *knowledge* is concerned, I cannot say that any one here is guilty . . . and, anyhow, what are you grumbling about? There's many a film star would pay through the nose to get half of what you've been having!

You're an odd person, but for once I can understand your feelings. It must have been extraordinary for you to have done that work on the Brunton Case without ever having even *seen* any one of the dramatis personæ. In order to fulfil your request to know what has happened to the players since the final 'person or persons unknown' of the Coroner's Jury, I should imagine that I have squandered quite a large amount of government money. Pike has been in charge of the job. Being a job for you, he has expended even more than his usual energy. The results of his inquiry have been tabulated and I send you a copy of the table herewith.

Please don't forget to let me know immediately you return to England.

Yours very sincerely,
E. G. Lucas

ENCLOSURE
Private and Confidential

REPORT RE MEMBERS OF BRUNTON HOUSEHOLD

I append hereunder a précis of the result of my investigations into the affairs of the various members of the household of the late Maxwell Brunton.

PRÉCIS

1. *Sidney Foljambe Harrison*, private secretary to deceased.—
For two weeks after the conclusion of the inquest, Harrison remained at 44 Rajah Gardens. He then left, in a hurry. The time he left coincided with the return from Cornwall of Mr Adrian Brunton. Mr A. B. had not been in the house more than ten minutes when Harrison left. The incident was reported to L.I. Division Headquarters by P.C. L.I. 428 Hardcastle. Hardcastle was going by 44 Rajah Gardens on his beat when the door opened and 'a man landed flat on his face on the pavement. He was immediately followed by a couple of suitcases and a trunk. Both the suitcases burst open.'

It is understood that Mrs Brunton was too ill to get rid of Harrison. Mr A. B. seems to have lost no time.

For a while Harrison was without work, and at one time, it is understood, was nearly destitute. He is now employed at the headquarters of the Society for the Promulgation of Reformation. He is in charge of the records department of the women's section. Pay: £2 15s. per week. Address: 34 Little Moscow Street, S.W.18.

2. and 3. *Arthur Jennings and Sarah Jennings*.—Arthur Jennings was re-arrested immediately after the conclusion of

the inquest—before he had left the court-room. He was sent to Park-hurst.

Sarah Jennings went into service, under her maiden name of Carpenter, at Stoke Manor, Fettering, Nr. Greyne.

Jennings had two years of his original sentence to serve with an extra year added after the charge of breaking prison. Recently, however, there has been a petition upon his behalf, and, although the decision of the Home Secretary has not yet been made public, it is understood here that he will be released, on special ticket-of-leave (contingent upon his good behaviour) within the next few weeks.

4. *Marie Jeannette Bocquet.*—It was difficult to trace this woman. She returned to Rajah Gardens after the inquest; but only for as long as it took her to pack her baggage. When this inquiry started it was found that we could pick up no trace of her during two months immediately following the inquest. After that period, however, she came again to the notice of the police. She was interested in the operation of a night club known as the *Tag and Bobtail.* At that time she was living with the proprietor of that club—Romano Forsitelli.

Bocquet left Forsitelli a few weeks ago, having taken up with Archibald (known as 'Doggie') Freeman—a third-class confidence man recently out after a term of four years.

Bocquet is under close observation, and it is the general opinion here that it will not be long before she is taken up.

5. *Mary Elizabeth Lamort.*—As has been notified in the Press, Miss Lamort was removed to hospital two days after the conclusion of the inquest, suffering from complete nervous prostration. She was in the Duchess of Falmouth's Nursing Home for seven weeks. She then proceeded to the South of France for a period of convalescent treatment which lasted seven or eight weeks, and has since removed to Los Angeles. It is understood that Miss Lamort is seeking film work in Hollywood. She has

publicly announced that her intention is to 'try and forget England.'

6. and 7.—*Claire Bayford and Peter Joliffe Hargreaves.*—There is little to report concerning Mrs Bayford and Hargreaves. One month after the inquest they were married—at the church of St. Giles-in-the-Wold, near Bitterhaven. The marriage was kept extremely secret and was, in fact, only generally known about at the commencement of this month.

8. *Adrian Brunton.*—From almost immediately after the time of the inquest until a fortnight ago, Mr Adrian Brunton continued to reside at 44 Rajah Gardens. He lived there alone except for two servants—Mrs Brunton (*q.v.*) having gone away upon account of illness.

Mr Adrian Brunton interested himself in the affairs in which his father's very considerable fortune had been invested. The opinion of the City in regard to Mr Adrian Brunton has undergone a great change. At the beginning he was, it is understood, regarded without any seriousness: now the general trend of opinion is to the reverse.

A fortnight ago Mr Brunton announced, via the daily press, his forthcoming marriage to Miss Susan Fanthorpe, the daughter of Mr Herbert Fanthorpe, the well-known stockbreeder.

The marriage was solemnised at the church of St. Mary's, Burton Hampstead. Mr Brunton and his wife are at present on the Continent. Mr Brunton has announced that on his return to England, he and Mrs Brunton are taking up their residence near Burton Hampstead. He will not continue in the City.

9. *Mrs Enid Brunton.*—After the conclusion of the inquest Mrs Enid Brunton returned to 44 Rajah Gardens. For six days she went about her house and affairs as if nothing had happened. Upon the seventh day she collapsed.

She was removed to the Dorset Nursing Home in Manchester

Square where she lay, for over ten days, in an extremely critical condition. She made a slow recovery. Approximately about a month ago, however, she returned to London from Italy and bought the lease of a small house near Regent's Park.

She is understood to be interesting herself (to the exclusion of all else) in the foundation of a new charitable organisation to be known as the Middle Class Protection Society.

A. P.

THE DETECTIVE STORY CLUB

THE SELECTION COMMITTEE HAS PLEASURE IN RECOMMENDING THE FOLLOWING NOVELS OF OUTSTANDING MERIT

"The Man with the Gun."

The Terror   EDGAR WALLACE

There are many imitators—but only one EDGAR WALLACE. *The Terror* is a most sensational thriller, and has had a great success both as a play and as a film.

The Leavenworth Case   ANNA K. GREEN

What did MR. BALDWIN say in 1928 ? He said : " *The Leavenworth Case* is one of the best detective stories ever written."

The Crime Club
By an Ex-Supt. of the C.I.D., SCOTLAND YARD

Here is the real straight thing from G.H.Q. A detective thriller that is different, by FRANK FROEST, the Scotland Yard man, assisted by GEORGE DILNOT, author of the *Famous Trials* Series.

Called Back   HUGH CONWAY

A clever and exciting thriller which has become world-famous.

The Perfect Crime   ISRAEL ZANGWILL

This very ingenious detective novel, by the distinguished novelist and play-wright, is the subject of one of the most successful films of the year.

The Blackmailers   EMILE GABORIAU

All detective writers worship at the shrine of Gaboriau—master of the French crime story. *The Blackmailers* is one of his best, replete with thrills and brilliantly told.

LOOK FOR THE MAN WITH THE GUN

THE DETECTIVE STORY CLUB

FOR DETECTIVE CONNOISSEURS

recommends

"The Man with the Gun."

The Murder of Roger Ackroyd

By AGATHA CHRISTIE

*T*HE MURDER OF ROGER ACKROYD is one of Mrs. Christie's most brilliant detective novels. As a play, under the title of *Alibi*, it enjoyed a long and successful run with Charles Laughton as the popular detective, Hercule Poirot. The novel has now been filmed, and its clever plot, skilful characterisation, and sparkling dialogue will make every one who sees the film want to read the book. M. Poirot, the hero of many brilliant pieces of detective deduction, comes out of his temporary retirement like a giant refreshed, to undertake the investigation of a peculiarly brutal and mysterious murder. Geniuses like Sherlock Holmes often find a use for faithful mediocrities like Dr. Watson, and by a coincidence it is the local doctor who follows Poirot round and himself tells the story. Furthermore, what seldom happens in these cases, he is instrumental in giving Poirot one of the most valuable clues to the mystery.

LOOK FOR THE MAN WITH THE GUN